*footnote;

A Literary Journal of History

• Various Authors •

Selected by Brendan Hamilton, Eric Shonkwiler, & Leah Angstman
Curated and Edited by Leah Angstman

Alternating Current Press
Boulder, Colorado

Footnote No. 4
Various Authors
©2018, 2020 Alternating Current

Alternating Current
Boulder, Colorado
alternatingcurrentarts.com

ISBN: 978-1-946580-19-1
First Edition: October 2018
First Print Edition: August 2020

The past changes a little
every time we retell it.
—Hilary Mantel

Letter from the Editor

Here we are again, dabbling in the past and bringing it to the future. As we go through an age of accountability and social justice as a society, the writing we're seeing becomes more aware, more prominent in its voicing of history's ill treatment of certain subsets of people and ideas. On these pages, we'll walk through some harsh realities, and we'll resurface as better people. Fiction and poetry have a way of bettering us; when mixed with history's ugly truths and imbalances, the result can change our minds forever toward the good.

We start right out with the gut punch of American slavery, hearing the voices of then and now, through Rev. Richard Allen, slavemasters, runaways, and Frederick Douglass, and leading up to Juneteenth, when enslaved workers in Texas finally learned that they'd already been free for two years. We'll meet Civil War zombies and cattle-hunting soldiers, and we'll go in search of the lost hoof of a famous fire horse. We'll explore the missionary failures of David Livingstone and Eleazar Wheelock and travel the seafaring journeys and shipwrecks of robber Joaquín Murrieta, arctic explorers, British lightermen, and one unfortunate girl in a rum keg. Women like Conchita Cintrón will have their firsts (and be arrested, naturally), and we'll unravel the dark mind of Virginia Woolf. We'll learn about the Brothertown Indians, the ill beginnings of Dartmouth College, and the massacres and stereotypes that Native Americans endured in the mid-to-late 1800s. We'll travel to England with Samson Occom, Dominic Fanning, Oliver Cromwell, nuclear bombs, and the erosion of the East Yorkshire coastline through the years. Art is explored through the eyes of Leda with her swan, Jacob Lawrence's Migration Series, the photography of the Great Depression, and Victorian photographs with dead people.

Featured Writer Kindra McDonald will take us through the Dismal Swamp and into the suicidal minds of Robert Frost and Meriwether Lewis, then through a history of salt, foot binding, and lost languages. Featured Writer Benjamin Goluboff examines the work and art curation of John Quinn and Walker Evans, the former responsible for the 1913 Armory Show that was the first exhibit of modern art, and the latter a renowned photographer of life in the 1930s.

And we'll resurface as better people. Let's go.

Table of Contents

Fiction

Nonfiction

Poetry

Featured Writers

Images

Matter

My Man Richard

*Trust no one till you have eaten
a bushel of salt with him.*
—German proverb

Vernita Hall

1783

Once he got saved, my man Richard could preach
hellfire out the devil. He could teach
honest to a judge, my slave. Impossible?
Well, I've learned his word is always gospel.
He's bought his freedom papers, eighteen months early.
I never seen a Negro with his hurry.
His hands sow profit. Seems all I grow is debt.
He plants friends and faith.
                                        I can't forget
I sold four of his blood. He'll probably never
see his mother again. Could you ever
forgive that act? Treat such a man as friend?

Well he served me fifteen years. Then
at our end, my slave offers a gift
to *me*, his master, Stokely Sturgis.
Salt. He give me *eighteen bushels.* (Y'understand,
that's half a year's wages for a common man.)
In consideration of "uncommon kind
treatment of his master." And my pride?
Much it cost my manhood to accept.
Dear is freedom. Cheap goes self-respect.
For the bargain price of   humbled   I could send
my two hundred acres toward the black again.
Richard—my redeemer. Catch the irony?
My former slave—a man more free than me.

Now he's free, he took a last name—Allen.
I know he knows a name don't make a man.
We parted equals. I shook the hand—a first—
of my man—my *friend* Richard, salt of the earth.

Stokely Sturgis'
Methodist Bible, 18th c.

11

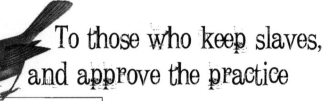

To those who keep slaves, and approve the practice

Rev. Richard Allen

written in 1794

The judicious part of mankind will think it unreasonable that a superior good conduct is looked for from our race, by those who stigmatize us as men, whose baseness is incurable, and may therefore be held in a state of servitude, that a merciful man would not doom a beast to; yet you try what you can to prevent our rising from a state of barbarism you represent us to be in, but we can tell you from a degree of experience that a black man, although reduced to the most abject state human nature is capable of, short of real madness, can think, reflect, and feel injuries, although it may not be with the same degree of keen resentment and revenge that you who have been and are our great oppressors would manifest if reduced to the pitiable condition of a slave.

We believe if you would try the experiment of taking a few black children, and cultivate their minds with the same care, and let them have the same prospect in view as to living in the world, as you would wish for your own children, you would find upon the trial, they were not inferior in mental endowments.

I do not wish to make you angry, but excite attention to consider how hateful slavery is in the sight of that God who hath destroyed kings and princes for their oppression of the poor slaves. Pharaoh and his princes with the posterity of king Saul, were destroyed by the protector and avenger of slaves. Would you not suppose the Israelites to be utterly unfit for freedom, and that it was impossible for them, to obtain to any degree of excellence? Their history shows how slavery had debased their spirits. Men must be willfully blind, and extremely partial, that cannot see the contrary effects of liberty and slavery upon the mind of man; I truly confess the vile habits often acquired in a state of servitude, are not easily thrown off; the example of the Israelites shows, who with all that Moses could do to reclaim them from it, still continued in their habits more or less; and why will you look for better from us, why will you look for grapes from thorns, or figs from thistles? It is in our posterity enjoying the same privileges with your own, that you ought to look for better things.

When you are pleaded with, do not you reply as Pharaoh did, "Wherefore do ye Moses and Aaron let the people from their work, behold the people of the land now are many, and you make them rest from their burthens." We wish you to consider that God himself was the first pleader of the cause of slaves.

That God who knows the hearts of all men, and the propensity of a slave to hate his oppressor, hath strictly forbidden it to his chosen people, "Thou shalt not abhor an Egyptian, because thou wast a stranger in his land."

Deut. 23.7. The meek and humble Jesus, the great pattern of humanity, and every other virtue that can adorn and dignify men, hath commanded to love our enemies, to do good to them that hate and despitefully use us. I feel the obligations, I wish to impress them on the minds of our colored brethren, and that we may all forgive you, as we wish to be forgiven, we think it a great mercy to have all anger and bitterness removed from our minds; I appeal to your own feelings, if it is not very disquieting to feel yourselves under dominion of wrathful disposition.

If you love your children, if you love your country, if you love the God of love, clear your hands from slaves, burthen not your children or your country with them, my heart has been sorry for the blood shed of the oppressors, as well as the oppressed, both appear guilty of each other's blood, in the sight of him who hath said, he that sheddeth man's blood, by man shall his blood be shed.

Will you, because you have reduced us to the unhappy condition our color is in, plead our incapacity for freedom, and our contented condition under oppression, as a sufficient cause for keeping us under the grievous yoke. I have shown the cause,—I will also show why they appear contented as they can in your sight, but the dreadful insurrections they have made when opportunity has offered, is enough to convince a reasonable man, that great uneasiness and not contentment, is the inhabitant of their hearts. God himself hath pleaded their cause, he hath from time to time raised up instruments for that purpose, sometimes mean and contemptible in your sight, at other times he hath used such as it hath pleased him, with whom you have not thought it beneath your dignity to contend. Many have need convinced of their error, condemned their former conduct, and become zealous advocates for the cause of those, whom you will not suffer to plead for themselves.

Rev. Richard Allen, c. 1799.
Lithograph by P. S. Duval, c. 1850.

Nights Spent Flying

DeMisty D. Bellinger

I've lost count of the days that I close my eyes against,
try to sleep in spite of the sunlight seeping through,
red globules dance across my sight

and this day is cooler than any days I've known.

I lay on a quilt I made with a woman called Rebecca,
a woman called Ruth,
and a woman we called ma'am because even though she was just like us,
she stood tall—
like us, she sewed for relaxation and knew enough to laugh
at doing work for pleasure

I close my eyes tighter and I can see their smiles, their high cheekbones.

The fat quarters were already worn bare and soft as brushed fresh cotton
when we got them, and the stuffing was only more scraps,
so the quilt was thin, and beneath it, I felt the prick of the grass tips,
the digs of the gravel

the grass and mud, cooling toward autumn.

Still, I was heading away and even in the light of day,
where I tried to sleep hiding beneath the trees of a hidden stand
I slept. I was learning to feel good. Heading away to a life of dreams

following a star like mythical wise men.

The Woman Was Leaving

DeMisty D. Bellinger

The woman was leaving—
Or staying
      I was the one leaving
            And after four miles, I will meet someone
A man maybe, and his wife
      The man is called Abel
            The wife is called Missus Abel and is sure to be there
The man will be white and wearing a large, woolen hat, black as the night
      I'd miss save for the light leaking from the moon
            He will ask, "Are ye lost?"
                I will say, "Sir, I believe I am."
                    Missus Abel will say, "I know the way."
Missus Abel will walk north and east,
      Abel will follow her,
            I will bring up the end.
              And when all is safe,
I will walk in the middle.

Slavery depicted in *Harper's New Monthly Magazine*, 1857.

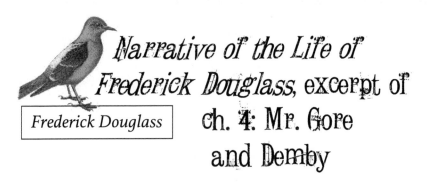

Narrative of the Life of Frederick Douglass, excerpt of

Frederick Douglass

ch. 4: Mr. Gore and Demby

written in 1845

Mr. Hopkins remained but a short time in the office of overseer. Why his career was so short, I do not know, but suppose he lacked the necessary severity to suit Colonel Lloyd. Mr. Hopkins was succeeded by Mr. Austin Gore, a man possessing, in an eminent degree, all those traits of character indispensable to what is called a first-rate overseer. Mr. Gore had served Colonel Lloyd, in the capacity of overseer, upon one of the out-farms, and had shown himself worthy of the high station of overseer upon the home or Great House Farm.

Mr. Gore was proud, ambitious, and persevering. He was artful, cruel, and obdurate. He was just the man for such a place, and it was just the place for such a man. It afforded scope for the full exercise of all his powers, and he seemed to be perfectly at home in it. He was one of those who could torture the slightest look, word, or gesture, on the part of the slave, into impudence, and would treat it accordingly. There must be no answering back to him; no explanation was allowed a slave, showing himself to have been wrongfully accused. Mr. Gore acted fully up to the maxim laid down by slaveholders,—"It is better that a dozen slaves should suffer under the lash, than that the overseer should be convicted, in the presence of the slaves, of having been at fault." No matter how innocent a slave might be— it availed him nothing, when accused by Mr. Gore of any misdemeanor. To be accused was to be convicted, and to be convicted was to be punished; the one always following the other with immutable certainty. To escape punishment was to escape accusation; and few slaves had the fortune to do either, under the overseership of Mr. Gore. He was just proud enough to demand the most debasing homage of the slave, and quite servile enough to crouch, himself, at the feet of the master. He was ambitious enough to be contented with nothing short of the highest rank of overseers, and per- severing enough to reach the height of his ambition. He was cruel enough to inflict the severest punishment, artful enough to descend to the lowest trickery, and obdurate enough to be insensible to the voice of a reproving conscience. He was, of all the overseers, the most dreaded by the slaves. His presence was painful; his eye flashed confusion; and seldom was his sharp, shrill voice heard, without producing horror and trembling in their ranks.

Mr. Gore was a grave man, and, though a young man, he indulged in no jokes, said no funny words, seldom smiled. His words were in perfect keeping with his looks, and his looks were in perfect keeping with his words. Overseers will sometimes indulge in a witty word, even with the slaves; not so with Mr. Gore. He spoke but to command, and commanded but to be obeyed; he dealt sparingly with his words, and bountifully with his whip, never using the former where the latter would answer as well. When he whipped, he seemed to do so from a sense of duty, and feared no consequences. He did nothing reluctantly, no matter how disagreeable; always at his post, never inconsistent. He never promised but to fulfil. He was, in a word, a man of the most inflexible firmness and stone-like coolness.

His savage barbarity was equalled [sic] only by the consummate coolness with which he committed the grossest and most savage deeds upon the slaves under his charge. Mr. Gore once undertook to whip one of Colonel Lloyd's slaves, by the name of Demby. He had given Demby but few stripes, when, to get rid of the scourging, he ran and plunged himself into a creek, and stood there at the depth of his shoulders, refusing to come out. Mr. Gore told him that he would give him three calls, and that, if he did not come out at the third call, he would shoot him. The first call was given. Demby made no response, but stood his ground. The second and third calls were given with the same result. Mr. Gore then, without consultation or deliberation with any one, not even giving Demby an additional call, raised his musket to his face, taking deadly aim at his standing victim, and in an instant poor Demby was no more. His mangled body sank out of sight, and blood and brains marked the water where he had stood.

A thrill of horror flashed through every soul upon the plantation, excepting Mr. Gore. He alone seemed cool and collected. He was asked by Colonel Lloyd and my old master, why he resorted to this extraordinary expedient. His reply was, (as well as I can remember,) that Demby had become unmanageable. He was setting a dangerous example to the other slaves,—one which, if suffered to pass without some such demonstration on his part, would finally lead to the total subversion of all rule and order upon the plantation. He argued that if one slave refused to be corrected, and escaped with his life, the other slaves would soon copy the example; the result of which would be, the freedom of the slaves, and the enslavement of the whites. Mr. Gore's defence [sic] was satisfactory. He was continued in his station as overseer upon the home plantation. His fame as an overseer went abroad. His horrid crime was not even submitted to judicial investigation. It was committed in the presence of slaves, and they of course could neither institute a suit, nor testify against him; and thus the guilty perpetrator of one of the bloodiest and most foul murders goes unwhipped of justice, and uncensured by the community in which he lives. Mr. Gore lived in St. Michael's, Talbot [C]ounty, Maryland, when I left there; and if he is still alive, he very probably lives there now; and if so, he is now, as he was then, as highly esteemed and as much respected as though his guilty soul had not been stained with his brother's blood.

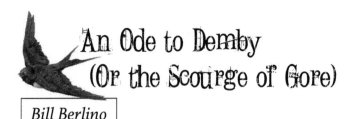

An Ode to Demby
(Or the Scourge of Gore)

Bill Berlino

Lashed to the gash,
defiant Demby dashed
from the Scourge of Gore,
through some underbrush,
then hurled himself,
headlong, into a stream,
to clean his beaten back.

As when Achilles retreated
(at Ilion, defeated)
to his ship by the sea,
where he knelt and wept
by the windswept Aegean,
grieving and heaving,
trying to console
his gore-ridden soul
after losing Briseis
(his soul's bride-to-be)
to the son of Atreus.

Frederick Douglass, c. 1850.

Torn by the decision—
revenge and oblivion
or self-preservation—
suddenly, *miraculously*,
Athene intervened
to resolve his conflicted soul.
(Or did she absolve
some unfulfilled vow?
Only Homer knows.)

Now Demby,
finding his feet
on the streambed,
surfaced his head
above the current,
then turned, slowly,
to stand his ground,
to face his cursed fate:
the grim gun of Gore,
who, from upon the shore,
ordered him to emerge,
on the count of three,
lest the sound of Gore's gun
become Demby's dirge.

And Demby,
shaking in the stream,
wrenched and weeping,
simply could not move;
he could not step forward
(to Douglass' horror)
without losing himself;
so, he held his ground—
proud, self-possessed,
innocent.

Alone,
he faced oblivion
(or his soul to be won)
at the antebellum count of three
(No deus ex machina; no Athene
to assuage Achilles' spleen,
to clean up the scene),
as Gore, safe upon the shore,
started the count aloud
before a stunned crowd.
And Demby, standing proud
(with tears, streaming down
his cheeks), stood his ground.

His time now up—at Gore's report;
Demby's brains and blood
began to dirty and flood
the pristine stream, flowing,
bright red, to the sea.

Was this the price
for an antebellum Dream?
Dirty Demby (no son of Peleus)
died clean.

Illustration from *Life and Times of Frederick Douglass*, Park Publishing Co., 1881.

Gore Shooting Demby

June 19, 1865

DeMisty D. Bellinger

emancipation has too many syllables and I don't have the words for syllables yet / I haven't the experience to understand what it could possibly mean and would be for me / major general has too many titles and none of them are master / he says free and some of us laugh / I step gingerly forward and nothing / for two years, major general granger says, we been free / and I take another step forward and I hear / nothing / I walk on and I don't even hear / a dog / I'm still walking.

Juneteenth announcement, The New York Times, July 7, 1865

FROM TEXAS

Important Orders by General Granger.

Surrender of Senator Johnson of Arkansas.

A SCATTERING OF REBEL OFFICIALS.

Our New-Orleans files bring us the following interesting news from Texas:

IMPORTANT ORDERS BY GEN. GRANGER.
THE SLAVES ALL FREE.
HEADQUARTERS DISTRICT OF TEXAS,
GALVESTON, Texas, June 19, 1865.

GENERAL ORDERS, NO. 3—The people of Texas are informed that, in accordance with a proclamation from the Executive of the United States, "all slaves are free." This involves an absolute equality of personal rights and rights of property between former masters and slaves, and the connection heretofore existing between them becomes that between employer and hired labor.

The freedmen are advised to remain quietly at their present homes, and work for wages. They are informed that they will not be allowed to collect at military posts, and that they will not be supported in idleness either there or elsewhere.

By command of Maj.-Gen. GRANGER.
F. W. EMERY, Major, and A. A. G.

Twenty Mile Dead

Robert Busby

That night an ice storm hit Twenty Mile, but only the bois d'arc anchored in front of the bait shop froze. Sleet packed the tree's limbs, and the limbs converged into a pair of boughs that plaited around the trunk and drove into the dry, red clay. Horseapples glazed with ice dangled from the bois d'arc, and the bug zapper hummed blue light against the glaze of ice. Otherwise, the heat remained oppressive, and the cicadas sang out beyond the loblolly pines and live oaks that crowded the bottom.

The others lay passed out in the shop, but Beauregard Eutuban, who was of Haitian descent, rocked on the concrete porch, watching the phenomenon unfold before him, a bottomless pickle jar of bourbon sweating into the cracks of his pale palms. Twenty Mile was a province of ghosts plopped down in a twenty-mile bottom. Beauregard had figured out that news quickly once he'd climbed out of his grave and walked a stretch of Twenty Mile Road before seeing his old friend and former master, Colonel Leon Claygardner, whom Beauregard himself had buried, living out of a canvas tent in the shade of a bois d'arc tree because it reminded Claygardner of his deceased parents. Col. Claygardner had scared the tent from a Union sergeant near Murfreesboro on his way home after catching an artillery shell in his chin at Campbell's Station in '63. While alive, the colonel had given Beauregard his freedom papers long before Emancipation, and that alone kept Beauregard for the next century and change in this afterlife with his old friend. Beauregard helped frame Claygardner's bait shop with hickory, and they used loblolly for the walls, and the newfound dead would arrive and either stay awhile or head down the rest of Twenty Mile for whatever came next.

Beauregard dropped his feet off an overturned milk crate, scattering playing cards onto the porch. Claygardner and he played gin rummy or bridge throughout the day but retired those for the thoughtless game of war when the last of the day would break behind the bois d'arc. The games and companionship were an amenity, to be sure. But what had really kept Beauregard here was this solitude on this porch between midnight and sunrise that Twenty Mile had afforded him for going on one hundred seventeen years now. Each evening after his fellow Twenty Milers turned in, Beauregard would rock on the porch and drink and imagine the rest of his son's life that Beauregard had not had the blessing to witness. Some nights he imagined Beauregard Eutuban, Jr., as the mayor of some small town in upper Illinois or a doctor practicing in Chicago. The owner of his own small business. He would have a good wife. A family to raise. Slave to no one.

Tonight, however, that solitude had been agitated. He'd been watching the phenomenon unfold for a good two hours before he'd taken to his feet on the porch, the blue Sunday suit in which he'd been buried draped down his long, skinny legs to just above his ankles, and drained the last finger from the pickle jar. His trance broke from the bois d'arc long enough to watch the vessel refill with strange magic and whiskey before he stepped off the porch to better absorb whatever had plagued the tree. After he made his hesitant way to the bois d'arc, he scraped a chunk of ice from its bark and dropped it into his drink. He reckoned he should've been happier he had ice for his bourbon now, but the last century seemed to have caught up with him overnight. Earlier in the evening, he'd had difficulty for the first time since his arrival in Twenty Mile imagining Junior as the owner of a dry goods store and its surrounding properties. Thought he had just been distracted by the tree, but he realized now that he could no longer recall what his son looked like. Could not recall his son's mother, either. Beauregard tried to conjure up grandchildren and great-grandchildren but had no memories to go from. The picture he summoned from his memory now was not of his boy. A hundred years had slowly evolved Junior's face into a hodgepodge of true memories and false memories that Beauregard could not differentiate.

If he'd just thought to have been buried with a photograph of his boy. Nothing deteriorated here except the mind.

•

The sun breached the horizon and found Beauregard still awake on the porch. Ominous memories Beauregard forgot he had forgotten but not why he had forgotten them encroached upon his thoughts now. His attempts to distract, such as trying to figure what was going on with that tree, were only half successful. Claygardner, whose parents' sudden disappearance had left him an orphan when he was twelve, had insisted the tree looked like his parents hugging. But Beauregard could see now that was foolish. They were clearly fighting or fornicating. Robins and mockingbirds joined a dove mourning the new day, and the first rays of light lit the belly of a cloud that hung over the bois d'arc where the thaw of the tree met the ubiquitous muggy heat of Twenty Mile. The sun would soon bake the place as had been its way for the duration of Beauregard's residency here.

Usually at this time, Jose McCullough, the half-Guatemalan proprietor of the shop, was up fixing breakfast. Before Twenty Mile, Jose had been the sous chef at Mi Pueblo, the only Mexican restaurant in Bodock. He'd insisted on breakfast every morning to Claygardner's approval, and Beauregard listened for the chef's racket in the kitchen. Nothing stirred behind him. He drained his glass again and instead heard the tennis shoes of their resident angler approaching from the path that cut down to the pond from the rear of the bait shop.

"Morning, Bobbie," Beauregard said.

Bobbie tipped her orange University of Tennessee cap. She was heavy-hipped, and her large breasts would have toppled a taller, skinnier woman. Every night, she retired after dinner to go night fishing. "Fell asleep. By that I mean I was passed out." Bobbie set a kitty-litter bucket half-full of catfish and pondwater down on the porch. "What's your excuse being up this early?"

"Contemplating."

"Uh huh." Bobbie nodded toward the bait shop. "Mi Pueblo got coffee brewed?"

"Didn't know he was up."

"Out back filling firewood into those empty grease drums. Got 'em arranged around that garden of his."

Jose had sown the garden from seeds he carried with him when his yellow pickup turned to a pat of soft butter against the grille of an eighteen-wheeler, the event that had landed him here.

"He think his tomatillos're gonna catch cold in this heat or something?" she said.

"Tree froze last night."

She regarded the tree for the first time. "Huh. Hell, see that now."

This being some locale nestled between their past life and—their best-case scenario—the purgatory of a forgiving God, Bobbie didn't question the bois d'arc suddenly freezing up in a climate that nudged at triple-digit temperatures any more than her fellow Twenty Milers had last night. Bobbie yanked a slick catfish from the bucket and plopped the specimen on the stump set off to the right of the porch. The catfish's white belly bellowed out from beneath the fish. A cleaver was lodged in the stump. Bobbie took the filet knife beside the cleaver and shaved a collar just above the gills.

Beauregard asked, "How come you ain't never gone on?"

Bobbie carved off the fins and flipped the catfish over, stenciled a line with the filet knife down the length of the fish's belly. "Gone on where?"

Beauregard nodded toward the back eleven miles of Twenty Mile Road.

"Huh." Bobbie gutted the fish and plopped its entrails on the porch and began on the next one. Later she would nail each fish to the side of the stump where she would peel off its skin. She had lived her whole life in Bodock and about knew everyone, which meant she knew of no woman there who shared her desires who would probably ever come down that road. So, Bobbie had settled for her other love. "Fishing ain't never been better. This life or the previous one or, hell, the next life, for all I know."

"You think Jose gonna ever move on?"

"You thinking about moving on?"

Beauregard never had that he'd known of. The only way into Twenty Mile was Twenty Mile Road. Most folks who died around Bodock eventually headed this way. That much they all knew. The bait shop sat somewhere around mile marker nine, and when confronted with the truth regarding their own mortality, the first instinct of most newcomers who arrived to Twenty Mile still in denial of their circumstances was to sprint back down Twenty Mile Road. Claygardner kept newcomers from returning to Bodock to roam as a specter among the living by a trap door that vivisected

24

the incoming road about a quarter mile from Twenty Mile. The door was rigged so that its release did not trigger on the way into Twenty Mile but would drop a would-be escapee right into an eight-foot ditch. No such physical obstacle kept Twenty Milers from continuing on to whatever destination lay beyond the twentieth mile. No such physical obstacle could. Claygardner had tried them all to little success in increasing the population of his fledgling ghost town.

"I been here near hundred twenty years," Beauregard said.

"Huh," Bobbie said, as she wedged the cleaver from the stump and hacked the tail off a third catfish still pulsing with life. The slick beast drained the last of itself down the tributaries of the barked stump. The angler dropped the tail on the stump for Jose to fry later. Bobbie said she had been convinced she was going to tuck tail the hell out of Twenty Mile in Jose's yellow pickup when he first arrived after the *Bodock Bi-Weekly* misattributed to Jose a crime of bestiality, and Bodock all but ran Jose McCullough, not Josh McCullough, from its borders. But before she braved wherever she would arrive after crossing the threshold of the twentieth mile, Bobbie had decided to tangle fishing line with the elusive catfish one last time. That evening she caught the twenty-pound specimen that had, Bobbie deduced, bullied inferior catfish from taking bait.

"Since then, caught damn near the equivalent of a bushel each day. Got myself a quiet stamp for fishing and no reason for nothing else. I'm happier than a lone prick in a well-staffed brothel."

To Claygardner, Twenty Mile was a secondhand Bodock, another attempt to build a burgeoning town of his own in what seemed the infinite acreage of an afterlife, all beneath the shade of his parents. Jose had been given the keys to a rundown, barely functional kitchen in a place he would never be run from. Beauregard had, what—glasses of whiskey that refilled at his volition and decades to rehash a family history he had not lived to see?

But now dark reminiscences that Beauregard had tethered to his unconscious knocked at his waking thoughts, free to fill the void of the slipping memories of his wife and Junior and all the grand offspring he had never seen. For the first time, Beauregard found himself contemplating his departure from Twenty Mile.

•

Around noon a flowing gown a mile away approached Twenty Mile. The promise of a woman of splendid curvature shrouded in a loose summer dress or a leg-slitted evening gown with a plunging neckline gathered the Twenty Milers on the porch, only to witness a bald, rotund man trudge the last tenth of a mile toward them. The man had clammy skin and a thick beard overwhelmed with gray hair. To the left of the porch, a fly buzzed its colleagues the coordinates of the rotting innards of catfish. The ice held tight to the bois d'arc and appeared as if the cold flora were breathing into the sweltering air.

The blue-patterned garment the newcomer wore kept the front of him modest. The back of him was left exposed. Back sweat carved tributaries in his dust-caked skin before converging into the crack of his ass. The humidity had all the men of Twenty Mile in a perpetual state of nut soup or swamp crotch, as it were, but the newcomer's garment did allow the enviable luxury of a breeze.

The man panted. "Back there. Looked like. Y'all's tree. Was on. Fire. Don't. So much. Up close."

The Twenty Milers watched the newcomer catch his breath.

Claygardner said, "Been meanin' to ask an expert once he came along what had afflicted my tree. What was you thinking, Beauregard?"

"Ain't nothin', Colonel," Beauregard said. "Just caught a cold. They be a'ight."

"That a hospital gown?" Bobbie asked.

"Yes," the newcomer said.

"Well," Bobbie said, looking around, seeing if anyone else wore the same glaring grin of epiphany. "That'd about explain it."

The newcomer said, "Explain what?" and asked the Twenty Milers to pardon him while he reached behind and held the gown closed. He scanned each of the four inhabitants of Twenty Mile and chuckled.

Col. Claygardner wore a straw slouch hat, and his gray, double-breasted shell jacket bore the yellow facings and insignia of mounted infantry that he'd stitched to his sleeves himself. Two stars on his collar, and the ammunition belt that slumped across his gaunt hips held an empty holster. His facial hair grew down from his ears but stopped even with his lips because of a distilling accident at the age of twenty. Jose had on his Mi Pueblo chef coat, baggy checkered pants, and a pair of grease-stained Nikes.

The newcomer said, "I must have stepped off into some sort of deep-fried collective unconscious. Are y'all all Southern archetypes? The Confederate, the slave, the Mexican immigrant."

"Guatemalan," Jose said. "Natural-born American."

The newcomer asked Bobbie, "Are you supposed to be some kinda lesbian Bill Dance?"

They invited the man into the bait shop for nourishment. Claygardner assumed his regular seat facing the door at his usual lopsided table where he crossed his legs and lapped his wide-brimmed hat over his knee. The blades of the ceiling fan creaked around their axle like a mud-bogged wagon wheel, and Beauregard had to push back against some old memory nudging into view.

Jose got started on the coffee to the satisfaction of Bobbie—who was still butchering the catfish—before disappearing behind the curtain to fire up the kitchen. For lunch, Jose fried over-easy huevos and catfish, served with a dollop of lime-cilantro mayonnaise. The newcomer introduced himself as Harold Fitch. Fitch had a wife of fifteen years that he "made love to" every Friday and two kids who attended Bodock Junior High, where Fitch served as school counselor to the tumultuously-hormoned student body. Last thing Fitch remembered was reclining on an oral surgeon's chair and counting down from one hundred. It was an outpatient surgery, but all four wisdom teeth needed to be cut from his gums rather than pulled. The surgeon knocked him out something good. Beauregard was unfamiliar with wisdom teeth. Bobbie determined they were the appendices of the mouth. "Got no teeth left," Claygardner said, his sock puppet mouth sunk down his face. "Wise or otherwise."

No one asked, but Claygardner retold for Fitch the time he fended off against Ambrose Burnside during the Yankee's Knoxville Campaign in '63 because the bastard northerner had plagiarized the distinctive architecture of Claygardner's beard. When Claygardner finished the story, Fitch confessed that he'd once sported a pair of sideburns in his regrettably more fashion-foolish days.

"A pair of what?" Claygardner asked incredulously.

"Sideburns," the newcomer said.

Claygardner slapped his slouch hat against the table, tugged at the handlebars of hair on his own jaw, and screamed irately that he could not fathom that the bastards in charge of naming things had named this fashion after that double-chinned son of a bitch. "Man brings nothing but terrible news," Claygardner said. "Let's send him back to Bodock, Beauregard." But Claygardner instead produced a pack of cards from a pouch in his hat. The cards from last night still lay scattered on the porch, but there was always a new pack each afternoon. "Then we can get back to our game. Damn noon, and we ain't played a hand yet."

The sound of Claygardner's voice now conjured some déjà vu of resentment in his old friend. Beauregard tried to stop himself but couldn't rein in the sudden contempt, the origin for which he hadn't yet formed the memory. "Was a shame," Beauregard said, "you trekking your flat ass clear 'cross Tennessee just so you could tickle yo' nuts over Ambrose's beard."

"Huh?" Claygardner asked.

"I mean, you ask nice," Beauregard said, "he mighta met you halfway."

Fitch asked, "What exact level of my unconscious have I stepped into?"

Beauregard had let himself go too far and invited Fitch out on the porch. There he said, "Don't mind the colonel. He just ill about that tree. Don't want to lose the shade it provide."

"I guess that makes a kind of sense," Fitch said but sounded uncertain. "An ice storm was supposed to land in Bodock the day after my procedure. I guess my unconscious projected the knowledge of that storm onto the tree."

Beauregard didn't know exactly what Fitch was saying but knew the newcomer was still confused and would have a hell of a time resigning himself to his fate. Fitch would require some help acclimating, so Beauregard invited him to sit, and when he did, Fitch did not concern himself with his modesty. His balls clung to a pasty thigh like a clapper welded to its bell. He set his drink behind him on the concrete porch.

Beauregard asked, "What do a counselor do exactly?"

Beauregard noticed that Fitch perked at the opportunity to discuss the subject of himself. He crossed his legs, sipped his rotgut, and caressed his beard before he explained that he counseled students on both general and specific instances of typical adolescent issues: bullying, puberty, low self-esteem stemming from acne or sudden weight gain due to hormonal imbalance, profanity as a declaration of maturity, lackadaisicalness, fondling the female form, the male form, the self-form, i.e., masturbating in bathroom stalls or locker rooms. Fitch threw in that he possessed a BA in psychology but had had to settle for a master's in counseling. Fitch's head dropped, and he looked where the hospital gown covered his chest like he could still feel the regret of that decision in his heart.

"My pacemaker," Fitch said.

"What's a pacemaker?"

"Got a bum ticker," Fitch said, pointed at his sternum. "A pacemaker's a device that keeps my heart from quitting suddenly—"

"Know what, man?" Beauregard said, hightailing toward any change in subject. "Got a dilemma you might counsel me on."

"Are you thinking about taking off?"

Beauregard coughed on his bourbon. "How did you know?"

Fitch's smirk loosened into a shit-eating grin. "That surly Confederate man owns you, right? As the archetypal slave, it's only natural you'd be led to believe yourself property. Therefore, to leave your owner would be to commit the Judeo-Christian sin of theft. Perhaps you even feel indebted to the Confederate for placing a roof over your head and food at your table. The clinical term is Stockholm Syndrome."

But Beauregard was only half listening. The memory of the moment when Beauregard realized that Claygardner had lied about freeing him had arisen from a dark corner of his mind. The moment had come only a year after the War began. Beauregard and Claygardner had formed their own company of mounted infantry, the men of which did not exist, with the sole purpose of smuggling goods for profit into Memphis. On the way to the Bluff, their wagon got stuck in some mud, and they were digging their way out when a lynch mob approached, figuring on coming across fugitive slaves. The mob spokesman had asked for papers on Beauregard but not on the stolen mount he was riding, and Beauregard remembered thinking they were in a heap of trouble. For years, Claygardner had assured Beauregard that his papers were in safekeeping in a lockbox at the Bodock Bank, which wouldn't do them much good, staring down those white hoods now. Without the authentic documentation that Beauregard was a free man, the two of them would have to blow themselves through that lynch mob best they could. Or at least die trying. But then Claygardner held up a hand in a truce. Draped back his overcoat slowlike. And instead of pulling a pistol, he handed over the papers still claiming his ownership of Beauregard.

"Since this is my own unconscious," Fitch said, "your dilemma must be the projection of some guilt of my own. I applied for a job at a rival high school recently and included in my résumé an acceptance into, and a significant amount of coursework completed toward, a second degree from Harvard. Really, I've only finished one psychology distant-learning correspondence course." Fitch shit-grinned his glass. "Not worried about confessing that to you, either, cause you're a figment of my imagination."

To Beauregard's left the neglected guts of Bobbie's catfish wafted their stench into the air. The bois d'arc still lofting fog in the immediate atmosphere that recalled for Beauregard every load of dirt that had been filled and slung from his spade digging Claygardner's grave beneath the family tree. The hatred that Beauregard had forgotten until right now on this very porch that he'd carried with him ever since his oldest pal had produced those papers.

He had a thought right then to say just fuck it. Why remain in Bodock if all good memories faded like the autumn leaves he hadn't seen in over a century? Because he wanted to remember why Claygardner had denied liberty for twenty-something years right to his only friend's face. Beauregard believed he needed to know that before he departed.

On the porch, Fitch blasted a fart unobstructed by clothing so that his ass cheeks flapped against the concrete. Fitch said the two of them should, for the foreseeable future, at least, concentrate on his own problems. This being his unconscious and all. He would be waking up soon, anyway. Then Beauregard would cease to exist. Until then, Fitch had to take a piss and was pretty certain a catheter would not have been implanted for an outpatient surgery. As such, he would urinate all down the dental chair.

"Obviously I'm not wearing a diaper," he said and pointed at the piss-boner pitched beneath his gown. "Perhaps I should just walk it off around the shop."

•

Dusk that evening punched cold back into the tree. Beauregard and Bobbie bookended the porch, bourbons in tow. More newcomers kicked dust now in the dirt lot in front of the shop. They had arrived throughout the afternoon: Monroe Brown, from complications due to stroke, and Major Harks still dressed in Trebark camouflage, who had been taken by general old age while sitting in a tree stand the day before the forecasted ice storm was to hit Bodock. Also, Baldwyn Galloway, a Civil War reenactor struck down on foot by an eighteen-wheeler. Claygardner took to the Civil War reenactor and, in between retelling his war experience, marveled at the way Baldwyn could make-up his face with pale red dirt and could distort his body to resemble a battlefield casualty. After one of his postmortem positions, Baldwyn suggested they ought to recreate tomorrow afternoon the whole of Claygardner's Civil War narrative.

Each of the newcomers said upon arrival that their deaths seemed obvious. Baldwyn regarded his mortality as a small payment to stand beside the idol he had for years worked his way up the ranks of his reenactment company to emulate. Fitch heard none of their discussions and wobbled on the porch in a stupor more drunken than any anesthesia could achieve. Red dust clung to an area of the gown where he had ended up pissing himself. Some of the flies from Bobbie's catfish remains decided to end it all in the electric blue of the bug zapper.

The dusk now froze any thaw that had occurred that afternoon, and the thaw caulked the wrinkles of the tree's branches, swelling the bois d'arc something arthritic. An hour later, Claygardner was inspecting the pistol

Baldwyn used for reenactments—to Claygardner's disappointment, the piece was not the .44 Colt Army Revolver he had carried, but a U.S. Aston single-shot smoothbore horse pistol—when one of the lower limbs of the bois d'arc gave and trembled against the ground.

Claygardner moaned and moved fast toward the bois d'arc. He picked up the limb and tried to fix it but abandoned the strategy when he couldn't get the branch to stay on the trunk. He diverted his efforts to holding up the other branches before they could be felled, too. The front brim of his slouch hat bent against the bark so that it appeared he was hugging the tree. The newcomers stood unsure what remedy to administer as Claygardner's tears froze his sideburns against the bark.

Bobbie had been a truck driver, and many of the goods she'd been hauling—a secondhand fryer, a diesel generator—powered the bait shop. The daylight-sensor floodlight she'd installed in a corner of the porch awning clicked on just above Beauregard's head as he saw a way to save the tree. But he didn't want to be the one to do it.

Bobbie waved Beauregard over, and Beauregard ambled around a swaying Fitch. "Ought to do something," Bobbie said. Beauregard walked Bobbie to the back of the shop.

Fitch was the only one to notice Beauregard slipping off and mumbled affirmation of his self-proclaimed genius. He wondered aloud why he had ever let his wife convince him of marriage and children and settling for his doughy life. Here before them was a savant, Fitch slurred, and slumped to the porch.

At the garden, Beauregard instructed Bobbie to balance one of the barrels on the rim of its base. She did, and the barrel began a drunken roll to the front of the bait shop. The wood Jose had chopped rattled around inside the grease drum.

"What in hell are you doing?" Jose stepped out and asked.

Beauregard said, "No ice is gon' plague your garden, man." As evidence, he pointed to many of the vines and stalks already sagging, not with ice but with their respective fruits. "So, you mind rolling another barrel around to the front?"

The newcomers offered their hands when they saw what the resident Twenty Milers were up to. Claygardner was moved to tears and worked flame into the barrels until all five were lit and standing vigil around the tree. Beauregard stood to the back of the crowd that waited in silence until ice dripped from the branches. Jose had retreated into the shop to prepare a victory feast for the small flood of customers who followed the excitement indoors. He'd laid out for them chorizo corn tacos made from venison that Major Harks had on his person and garnishes of tomatillo salsa and cilantro. Accompanying the tacos were guacamole with avocados, tomatoes, red onions, and limes from the garden, and elote with mayonnaise, chili powder, and a squeeze of lime lathered over the corn cobs. Bobbie pardoned herself from a sit-down supper and took hers to spend the evening alone on the pond banks. Beauregard didn't know how to move his feet beyond the perimeter of light spilling from the bait shop porch.

Claygardner had hung back in the dirt lot, as well, while the rest of

Twenty Mile retired to supper. "Finally got us two more skilled in card playing. Harks and Monroe's both experienced in bridge and poker. Can finally extend our repertoire." When Beauregard didn't respond, Claygardner said to his back, "Heard you been contemplating this morning."

Beauregard faced Claygardner. "Bobbie got a mouth like a damn catfish."

"The angler?" Claygardner asked. "Hell, Fitch told me. Said himself was a liber-tay-rian? Whatever the hell that is. Concerned with rightful property and whatnot. Who else did you not confide in besides me?"

Beauregard took a minute finding the words: "Well, couple more card games just gonna mean a couple more ways I could wipe your ass each morning."

"Mean you ain't tired yet of cleaning another man's shit chute?"

Beauregard shrugged. "What's friends for if not to deny another his freedom and then lie about it?"

"Emancipation was gonna free you anyway."

"Twenty-five fuckin' years after you was already said to of," Beauregard said. "Fuck you, Leon. Just 'cause you convinced that your parents turned into trees 'stead of facing the fact they left you, don't mean I or any other sumbitch on God's creation gotta stick around and be your therapy group."

"What's a therapy group?"

"I dunno, something the newcomer said." Beauregard walked out into the dirt some more before he stopped and pointed at the gnarled bois d'arc. "You know it look like they fuckin', right?"

"Wish I could not allow it. Believe me when I say I do regret not authenticating your official release from servitude while alive and that, if I had some similar something to keep you here now, I'd gladly repeat the mistake."

Beauregard didn't know what to say to that. Was he supposed to feel sorry just because Claygardner had staked here in Twenty Mile and had to watch all manner of folks decide they didn't see in this place what Claygardner did? Beauregard had despised all of them and despised himself now for any sympathy he held for his centuries-old companion and for allowing himself to endure—or for allowing whatever power had been the agent in him enduring—the betrayal by burying the knowledge of it so that he could without guilt accept what Twenty Mile offered him.

"How'd you do it?" Beauregard asked. "How'd you block my memory?"

Before Claygardner could answer, the thought arrived at Beauregard that he'd never see his old pal again. He hoped this memory wouldn't follow him where he was going. He hoped no memory followed him.

"Nevermind," Beauregard said. "I don't wanna know."

"A'ight. Shit, you ought to know, you leave it seems I'm fixing to get a replacement to beat me in cards for the next century or so, anyway."

"Come again?"

Claygardner nodded at the bait shop. "Monroe in there said he worked his entire life selling furniture for a man that looked like you. Same name as yours, too. Said that that Eutuban owned a lumberyard and a quarry and a furniture plant. Lot of land."

"No shit."

"Nope. Guess your kinfolk made it in Bodock, after all."

The muscles in Beauregard's neck clenched his Adam's apple. He wanted to meet his kin, but he also feared the pull it would have on him staying, which he could no longer abide. And how would he even know that the arrival of a grandson wasn't another of Claygardner's horseshit tricks to keep Beauregard by his side for all eternity? Beauregard didn't trust his old pal to let him ever leave and figured the colonel would do or say anything to keep Beauregard with him. Beauregard needed a diversion.

His eyes landed on Fitch, passed out some feet from the catfish innards. Beauregard studied the form until another idea blessed him. He told Claygardner to hold on a minute and walked into the bait shop to borrow a disposable razor from Jose's shaving kit. Beauregard returned with a bowl of cold water and shaved Fitch's chin. He left the sideburns curving up into his mustache in the Ambrose fashion. Then he aided Fitch to his feet, leaned him against a four-by-four column, and gave Claygardner the word like so many pranks Claygardner and he had pulled over the years on those newcomers they didn't like or who'd possessed the misfortune of stumbling into Twenty Mile during a streak of boredom, of which there were many. Claygardner drew the blank-loaded pistol he had not returned to Baldwyn.

"You know I never gave a damn about Ambrose's whiskers, right?" Claygardner said.

"Right."

"I was just et up with guilt."

Beauregard nodded and let the colonel keep his lie and dignity. He watched Claygardner aim at Fitch through the belching flames of two oil barrels.

Claygardner yelled to the counselor, "Ya dead, son! Welcome to hell!"

The lids of Fitch's eyes lifted, then widened with recognition. Claygardner cocked the hammer, pulled the trigger. The pistol pissed fire and farted smoke into the holdout of cold air that still fought for territory around the bois d'arc. Fitch slipped backward onto the porch and landed on his back. From there, he reached behind him where he felt the pile of catfish guts his head had landed in.

"Oh, shit! Oh, shit!" Fitch yelled and took off like some blue-caped, near-nude banshee back toward Bodock. He screamed about the slave-owner having blown his goddamn genius brains out. A cloud of gravel dust chased behind him.

Beauregard had already aimed himself in the opposite direction, toward mile marker ten. He did not turn to see the entertainment bring the newcomers back onto the porch, whiskey-handed and jaws still gnawing mouthfuls of their intermitted feast.

Cattle

Roger Sippl

Los Angeles, 1862

With the light of his new oil lamp, Governor Stanford
reads the weather report in the *Star:*
"On Tuesday last the sun made its appearance.
The phenomenon lasted several minutes
and was witnessed by a great number of persons."

It is rumored that the once-flourishing settlement
of Anaheim is completely destroyed,
and the few buildings that marked the
collective center for the ranchos of Los Angeles
have been overturned or broken apart.

When the flooding began,
the farmers gathered their turkeys into a shelter.
Now the water is deep, and the cattle
are difficult to shelter. When they are located,
they are seen panicked to stampede,
although their hooves just touch the mud.
They keep trying to run until finally they disappear.

Dana Point, 1835

In the warm morning fog,
a New England sailing vessel
carefully ties to short pilings in the cove.
As several men hoist a long boat,
they hear the hollering of dying cattle
and the crack of sledgehammers.
Like heavy carpets the wet skins fall from the cliff.
The men are careful not to overload the boat.

Santa Catalina Island, 1864

They hear the random clanging of a small bell,
the Union soldiers row from their cruiser;
they climb the cliff to find the cattle,
the cattle that are thin like goats.

Vegetation of the island is sparse,
but wild currants, mashed cactus juices,
and occasional sea lions could support a man
or a group of men; only officers leave the ship.

Two uniformed marksmen fall to their right knees
and aim at the cow's forehead. The animal falls
while still chewing something. They tow the cow
to the ship in a boat of its own.

While unloading, the boat capsizes.
The cow sinks into clear, black water.

19th c. woodcut of Union
soldiers butchering cattle to
feed the army.

The Lost Hoof of Fire Horse #12

J. Bowers

The Hoof

"No hoof, no horse," horse people say, tucking each leg between their knees, fingers scanning for cracks in the keratin, bad pasterns, or thick rings of bone. This quadripartite handshake has continued for 5,500 years. It is a ritual repeated throughout each animal's lifetime, verdict changing with time and care.

But here is no horse, just hoof—the left hind leg of a half-Percheron mare, to be precise, dead since March 1890. Trotted out for photographs, the lost hoof of fire horse #12 rests on spotless cotton as Smithsonian interns Instagram it into the datasphere, now reaching white gloves into frame, now turning the artifact gently toward the light. Its black preservative coating glistens like wet licorice under the fluorescent hum.

Stabled in a metal cabinet at the National Museum of Natural History's archives for more than a century, the lost hoof of fire horse #12 has a drawer all to itself, filed between ambergris and mammoth teeth. Its final shoe remains attached by a lone nail, the black metal U torqued ninety degrees away from where the farrier nailed it on, now become a C. Three other nails tore through the hoof wall, dislodged by velocity, while friction bent the two remaining back against the shoe, tips jabbed accusingly at the holes they flew from, leaving dark dents in the corium. Cauterized at the ankle soon after its retrieval from the streets of our nation's flammable capital, the hoof was dunked, shoe and all, in black gutta-percha for safekeeping: a gory candy apple.

The uniformity of the severed limb's tarry coating somewhat softens its surgical horror. This was District Fire Chief R. W. Dutton's first thought upon receiving the finished *objet d'art*, wrapped in butcher paper inside a wooden crate and smelling strongly of molten rubber. His second thought, after it was unpacked onto his desk, was that the lost hoof of fire horse #12 would make an intriguing paperweight—something for reporters and government officials to mention whenever they visited his office.

He was right. Whenever anyone came to see him, Chief Dutton launched into a stump speech about the marvelous fidelity of the horses in his employ. Eyes welling, he'd explain how this hoof was amputated alive from its noble owner in the line of duty—how that incredible horse galloped eight more blocks on the bloody stump left behind, so pure was its desire to save humans from four-alarm hellfire. Once his listeners were groping for handkerchiefs, Chief Dutton artfully segued into an explanation of why the department needed upward of seventy head per annum, to replace those unfortunate horses who gave all and asked so little in return.

"A steam engine won't die to save your life," Chief would intone, gaveling the hoof on stacked ledgers for emphasis. "A fire horse will."

Thus, the lost hoof of fire horse #12 filled municipal coffers for years upon years, tax dollars buying colt upon colt to fling at the greedy flames.

But removed from the long-gone context of Chief Dutton's desk, the lost hoof of fire horse #12 does not curate neatly. For over a century now, it has, like so much American detritus, been deemed worthy of preservation but not display. Unlike the gawping coyotes and pickled squids in the National Museum of Natural History's collection, which, having died whole, are shown so, a lone hoof can't be shoehorned into a timeline about evolution, nor blend unobtrusively into a Great Plains diorama. It turns out that dismemberment requires a longer explanation than what fits on a standard museum label. The lost hoof of fire horse #12 demands its own vitrine, alcove, and motion-sensitive spotlight, all luxuries the Smithsonian Institution cannot spare in the age of interactive edutainment.

In truth, the hoof has never been family-friendly. The earliest recorded evidence of its presence at the National Museum of Natural History appears in a May 1902 *Washington Post* article titled "Story of an Equine Hero: Famous Run of Fire Engine Horse to Be Perpetuated." In this short item, Professor Samuel Pierpont Langley, renowned aviator and third Secretary of the Smithsonian Institution, tactfully rejects Chief Dutton's request that the hoof be placed on permanent public display.

"At some future time it might be thought best to place on exhibition a case of objects illustrating the work of the fire department, when it would, of course, be proper to include the hoof," avers Langley, taking pains to praise the "wonderful endurance" of the animal and to concede its demise indeed "one of the incidents of the history of the horse which deserved to be preserved."

Chief Dutton, who was by that point more interested in acquiring a herd of steam-powered fire engines than perpetuating the useful myth of the loyal fire horse, accepted Langley's refusal without protest. Thus, his macabre paperweight was first consigned to "the nation's attic," which is really a basement, attics being notoriously bad places to preserve anything.

•

The Horse

City records detail that this particular fire horse #12 pulled the No. 3 Company's second hose-cart from August 1887 to March 1890, a short but average tenure for the high-risk career of a sentient urban emergency vehicle.

Hand-selected at auction by Chief Dutton, this #12 was a compact gray Percheron mare with a docked tail, chopped short at the root soon after birth. Besides being sufficiently fancy for parades, gray horses were easier for pedestrians to spot in the dark, when engines hurtled top speed through gaslit streets toward distant flames. Chief Dutton liked to keep the capital city's herd at around two hundred head, since it wasn't unusual to lose a few horses each month to disease, lameness, colic, or some other infirmity.

On average, just one out of twenty horses made the grade, and even these couldn't take the strain of service for more than a decade or so. If sound, some had second careers pulling omnibuses or delivery carts. But fire horse training was a deep spell, carved hard. Newspapers across the country regularly reported retirees bolting at the distant clang of station bells, completely forgetting the poor milkmen behind the reins in their mad, mothlike dash toward the flames.

It took a rare one. Fire horses had to observe a grueling halt, flight instinct overridden, as spidery harnesses fell from dark rafters, got strapped to trembling chests. Then the double door was flung wide, launching the blinkered teams into the cobbled streets, wheels tipping around corners and brass fittings flashing, the horses' trust utterly vested in the shouting driver who aimed them, galloping, toward smoke and fire.

For #12 that was Jack Knox, a good-hearted young fellow with a face like a shovel. During the long hours when buildings weren't on fire, #12 dozed with him in her stall. While clean, the stable of No. 3 Engine Company was a far cry from the ideal equine habitat painted behind the Smithsonian's prairie diorama, with its amber waves of grain in the middle distance, smudged mustangs' triangular heads bent earthward in greedy supplication. Fire horse #12 was well kept, by the standards then accepted for urban livestock. Knox saw to it that her bedding was dry; she received ample salt, oats, and hay, and a walk around the block on days the engines didn't run.

But cities give animals strange ideas—limn instinct with odd impulse. For example, fire horse #12 spooked at any tree taller than the caged sidewalk saplings she was used to galloping past. Simultaneously, she was known to doze unfazed near raging infernos while hot sparks rained upon her white-starred face.

The fire that killed #12 was four-alarm, with long orange geysers of flame spouting from the attic of a brick tenement like an infernal crown. Escaped tenants stood aloof across the street, swaddled babies in full squall as the crowd watched the No. 3 Engine joust the blaze. It was an average disaster, blamed on a drunkard with a lit pipe on a horsehair mattress. The unintentional arsonist was the only casualty besides fire horse #12, shot at the scene after Jack Knox found his charge hopping in the gutter on just three good legs.

"To be viewed as reliable by the public," said Chief Dutton, presiding over the shell-shocked company back at the station, "our fair capital's fire horses must appear an infinite herd, a unified faceless machine, ever ready to renew itself, like the army or the police. Sentimentality endangers confidence. Instead of eulogizing one horse, let us all be grateful that tonight, Death spared us all."

There followed a moment of silence that lasted exactly as long as it took for the No. 3 Company to realize Chief Dutton was finished talking. He took his time ascending the stairs to his office, pausing several times for gravitas. Then someone whooped, cards and beer emerged, and Jack Knox realized he was expected to pass the wee hours toasting a fire well doused, as though no great tragedy had occurred, as though he hadn't begun each morning for the past three years by pressing his cheek against Queenie's broad belly to listen for the secret aquarium of her gut. He could not un-hear its healthy gurgle, or the toothy clash of cobblestone on bone. He could not unsee the meaty insides of her left hind as he shrouded her for the knackers, tarpaulin flapping in the breeze.

He remembered Queenie and King snorting as nightcapped citizens clung to doorways to watch the hose-cart clatter past. As usual, Knox had leaned into the corners, balanced half-crouched behind his surging team, traces flying. He never slowed, or pulled up, or took notice of Queenie's injury beyond the awful observation that she was dragging somewhat, which made him drive her harder. There was only room in his throbbing head for *fire* and *faster* and *go*.

It stands to reason that losing an entire hoof from the fetlock down should make a horse limp or scream or collapse under itself, but Queenie ran on—she was just that brave or dumb or terrified.

•

The Hoof

The death of fire horse #12 reads like the noble sacrifice Chief Dutton wanted it remembered as, until one realizes, as Knox must have, that the mare *couldn't* have stopped galloping even if she'd wanted to, yoked as she was to King.

Picture the appendage wedged upright between the trolley rails, shin-bone a stick in a steel river. That's how Knox, unintentional prince of this morbid equestrian Cinderella, expected to find the lost hoof of fire horse #12. Given the preserved hoof's appearance today, it is more likely that Queenie's horseshoe got caught between the rail and the planking, after which the centrifugal force of the team's unstoppable gallop resulted in spontaneous amputation.

What's clear is how fast (by 19th-century standards) the death of fire horse #12 became a topic of national debate. In an April 1890 editorial reprinted nationwide, minor newspaper magnate and self-proclaimed "wild, woolly Westener [sic]," T. E. Goodrich of Shelbyville, Indiana, heaped "shame upon Washington" on the maltreated mare's behalf.

"An 'equine hero' indeed was that horse, but what of the man who had him [sic] shot? What of a city government that would permit such an act?" wrote Goodrich, with the armchair confidence distance affords. "Here in the 'Wild Woolly West,' an animal so faithful, so true, so noble as the poor beast your fire department slaughtered after it had performed a service never before equaled, would have had its wound bandaged, healed, and made as near perfect as possible: then, in place of blowing its brains out, it would have been furnished comfortable quarters for the remainder of its life. An intelligent people hang their heads in shame to think such a deed would ever be thought of in the Capital City of the grandest country God ever blessed."

Given the sheer number of broken-down ponies shot throughout the American West, Goodrich's words are obvious hyperbole. His manic screed does, however, suggest why Chief Dutton had his curious paper-weight entombed at the Smithsonian Institution in 1902—twelve years after the rest of #12 was buried—instead of chucking the hoof once it, like the horse, had outlived usefulness. Dutton knew trying to honor the relic in some official capacity was more politic than dealing with people like T. E. Goodrich inquiring as to its whereabouts.

Though the hoof of fire horse #12 appears solid and uniform from the outside, while alive it encapsulated a dozen interconnected anatomical structures, which in turn nourished a host of opportunistic bacteria and fungi. The horse's evolution from multi-toed quadruped to single-toed ungulate is a popular museum subject, as ample fossil records exist for all known iterations of the equine appendage, revealing how the last toe slid upward over millennia, then shrunk into the dime-sized discs of keratin still seen on the inner thighs of *Equus caballus*. The remaining digits fused, cornifying into layers of outer wall and inner capsule that could be seen even now if the desiccated hoof of fire horse #12 were sawn in half, like an Easter ham.

Each hoof is a calendar recording winter and spring, famine and feast, its structure as profoundly affected by moisture as the rolling grasslands it evolved to tread. Too much rain lets thrush fester in the clefts. Drought leads to contraction and sandcracks. Knowing this as everyone did in horse-powered America, the drivers of No. 3 Engine Company performed strengthening rituals based on science and superstition alike. They painted on neatsfoot oil, a pale-yellow unguent made by boiling cows' feet until they liquefy, hoof for a hoof. Witch hazel and arnica were rubbed into fetlocks. Pulverized shells from the local oyster den got stirred into bran mash.

Jack Knox's own tender podiatry remains evident today, as the lost hoof of fire horse #12 sports the smooth groove of a phonograph record, strong rings of horn accreted monthly. Read like a palm, the hoof's surface indicates that up until that last awful second, the horse attached to it was well fed and cared for, maybe even a little bit loved.

•

The Horse

Jack Knox couldn't rescue fire horse #12, so he saved her hoof instead. His reasons for doing so are murky. Maybe he had to return the appendage to the station to forgive himself for not driving the whole horse back. Maybe he wanted to show his fellow hose-cart drivers exactly how trolley tracks could mangle a good animal, warn them against getting too cocky behind the reins. Regardless of his motivations, surely "interesting paperweight" wasn't Knox's immediate intention when he snatched the lost hoof of fire horse #12 out of the gutter and tucked it, damp and bloody, under his coat flap.

Imagine the Chief's horrorstruck expression when Knox plonked the hoof onto his desk papers like a butcher's bone, a gauntlet, a dare. Such devotion made tossing it down the rubbish chute a non-option. Keeping it was the only fair answer. So in the end, Chief Dutton ended up having to save fire horse #12, too, whether he wanted to or not, and so did Professor Samuel Pierpont Langley of the Smithsonian Institution, and so do its white-gloved interns, and so do we, breathing at a glowing hoof on a computer screen.

If souls are real and horses have them, then it's nice to think how the soul of fire horse #12 might still be attached to her leftover hoof, tethered to it like a metaphysical balloon. Even in her spectral state, the gray mare might relish the dark silence of her subterranean tomb, or at least find it familiar.

After all, in life she was used to being stored, stowed, and saved for later—for that is what it was to be stabled in the basement box stalls of No. 3 Engine Company, forever edgy for the bell.

The hoof of fire horse #12, as archived in the National Museum of Natural History, c. 1902.

ABOVE:
Smithsonian catalog card for the admission of the hoof of fire horse #12 into their collection, May 1902.

ABOVE:
Fire horses of Engine Co. 9, Los Angeles, c. 1910.

RIGHT:
Mack the Noble Fire Horse, a famous horse of the Rescue Fire Co. in York, Pennsylvania, c. 1890s.

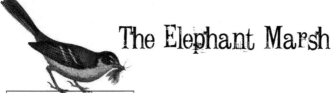

The Elephant Marsh

David Whorley

Dr. John Kirk, GCMG, KCB, FRS

For so long I admired him,
and found my ways to overlook
that great fanatic's optimism.
Among hard-earned discoveries
I found that cruelty and the visionary
were symbiotic species,
though never sent that news to Kew.
Eventually, I simply thought him mad.
But that was Livingstone.
We dragged worm-eaten boats like oxen
up dry rivers just to gain
a few more useless feet each day.
In '61 we lugged that tub
through the Elephant Marsh,
driven by his mania.

Now, two years on, we once again
were stranded in that place.
Reptilian eyes watched impassively
beneath the clouds of malarial flies.
But with no fuel for *Pioneer*
and low water on the Shiré,
we were paralyzed.
He raged, and called upon the wrath
of God to blast that place from Earth.
On shore, the feeding beasts flapped ears,
sniffed wind, and looked on quizzically.
I thought again of climbing
Morambala, far above that farce,
where Shiré and Zambezi meet.
Those days I lived for botany.
But he'd refused and, sensing how
I'd changed, wanted to be hurtful.
He pressed us on instead,
and Morambala drifted by,
silent and reproachful.
Stalled within the marsh once more,
we waited.

The gentle bumps upon the hull
did not at first attract attention.
But their soft insistence slowly
roused me from my sleep.
Through morning mist I saw
the river brought companionship
by filling up the marsh with corpses,
an outrage spawned by mass starvation.
The crocodiles soon stirred,
commenced their thrashing work
of ripping limb from limb.
It held me fast, both at the rail
and at the map edge of myself
where all becomes bare speculation,
where every river chokes with dead
and paddlewheels chunk and churn
all day, and everything is made
the meat for beasts of earth and air.
And he would die out there,
his heart cut out and buried on a trail,
his carcass dragged to Bagamoyo.

Eventually the waters rose.
We touched the shore, collected wood,
refired the boiler, and pushed upstream.

Sir John Kirk, 1908.

David Livingstone,
1864.

Illustration from David Livingstone's *Missionary Travels and Researches in South Africa, Including a Sketch of Sixteen Years' Residence in the Interior of Africa, and a Journey from the Cape of Good Hope to Loanda on the West Coast, Thence across the Continent, Down the River Zambesi, to the Eastern Ocean* (John Murray, London, 1857).

Illustration featuring the *Pioneer*, from David Livingstone's *Narrative of an Expedition to the Zambesi and Its Tributaries, and of the Discovery of the Lakes Shirwa* [sic] *and Nyassa* [sic], *1858-1864* (John Murray, London, 1865).

Letters & Excerpts, 1863

David Livingstone

Letter to the editor of the Medical Times and Gazette, written January 26, 1863, published August 1863

[. . .] Horror seems to lay hold on you at the bare mention of "Elephant Swamp." I am actually to pass through it to-morrow [sic], and am only sorry that the enormous herds of elephants—we have seen eight hundred in it at once—have become so knowing we have no chance of getting a steak or a foot. But see the effects of bad example: my imagination, do as I will to prevent it, obstinately pictures you sitting on that wilderness of eight hundred cesspools, which the commissioners only the other day swept away, and drinking water mixed, according to Dr. Acland, with all the abominations and unutterable filthinesses which are poured out of Oxford, Reading, etc., into your cup. Oh! you filter your water through a few inches of sand, do you? I would not trust it (unless I were in London) though filtered through the Great Sahara. The delicious unconsciousness with which you exclaim "Elephant Marsh; good heavens! what a vista of deep swamp, rotting vegetation, flies, vermin, stinks, agues, and dysentery do the words call up!" only excite a merry laugh, which I beg you to believe has not one particle of ill-nature in it, and the quotation, "Oh, wad some power the giftie gie us, / To see oursels as others see us [all sic]." You have actually a larger area of cesspool and marsh around and above London than exists in the Elephant Swamp, and to the direful effects let typhus, typhoid, diphtheria, cholera, consumption, scrofula, etc., testify. Here they are absolutely unknown. But our fever, if ill-treated, as by bleedings, or not treated, as it was in the case of the missionaries at Lynyanti, who took only a little Dover's powder, is as fatal as any two in your catalogue. And while it would be "penny wise and pound foolish" to make missionaries of inferior men, good men ought invariably to be accompanied by a thoroughly educated and well-paid Medical officer.　　　　　　　　　　　　　　　　I am, &c.

•

Excerpt from A Popular Account of Dr. Livingstone's Expedition to the Zambesi [. . .], written 1863, published 1875

The sight and smell of dead bodies was everywhere. Many skeletons lay beside the path, where in their weakness they had fallen and expired. Ghastly living forms of boys and girls, with dull dead eyes, were crouching beside some of the huts. A few more miserable days of their terrible hunger, and they would be with the dead.

Oppressed with the shocking scenes around, we visited the Bishop's grave; and though it matters little where a good Christian's ashes rest, yet it was with sadness that we thought over the hopes which [sic] had clustered around him, as he left the classic grounds of Cambridge, all now buried in this wild place. How it would have torn his kindly heart to witness the sights we were now forced to see!

In giving vent to the natural feelings of regret, that a man so eminently endowed and learned, as was Bishop MacKenzie, should have been so soon cut off, some have expressed an opinion that it was wrong to use an instrument so valuable *merely* to convert the heathen. [. . .] An ordinary clergyman, however well suited for a parish, will not, without special training, make a Missionary[. . . .]

•

Letter to Robert M. Livingstone, written February 20, 1863

[. . .] In ascending this river with the *Lady Nyassa* in tow alongside, we had no difficulty till we got to the Elephant [M]arsh, and there in sudden bends we found it an ackward [sic] matter to get along, for two vessels cannot be turned so quickly as one, and *Lady Nyassa* being pretty deep would go aground, and was very difficult to get off. Further up the river had risen only one foot eleven inches instead of about three feet, so we have lost more time than we anticipated. But no important work is ever accomplished without considerable trouble. We found that slave hunting and famine had produced fearful effects during our absence. We counted about thirty two dead bodies floating down as we came up. The smiling villages where we could last year have bought any amount of provisions are now all burned and we saw only a few starving people trying to save themselves from starving by fishing and collecting the seeds of grasses. Indeed our work will be greatly increased for now we must get all our provisions for ourselves & workmen from great distances[.]

[T]o me this retension [sic] of the slave trade is a great affliction. It destroys my hopes of benefitting [sic] the natives of the lower Shiré, and I only trust that we may do some good service on Lake Nyassa [sic]. The Tette people began the work of depopulation on our footsteps, then a half caste called Mariano devastated the country around Mount Clarendon. The loss of life has been fearful. Others have made slave forays in other directions, and no Governor interferes until the culprit is rich enough to be squeezed. He is fined and allowed to begin again at his old trade of slave hunting. The reason why no resistance can be made by the people themselves is Bows and arrows are nothing to guns and anyone with a few muskets & slaves may begin slavehunting. On the west coast Lord Palmerston put a squadron of men of war to stop the slave trade, and allow civilisation [sic] to begin its operations. Twenty missions were established, and twenty dialects reduced to writing. [S]ome twelve thousand communicants have been received into different churches, and thousands are educated. [. . .]

The Nurseryman

Arthur Allen

: A little bundle
of the tryeing of the Arctic Air.

How strange fortunes wee passed in farthest distant *Ultima Thula;*

The principle navigations & discoveries of the lost voyage to META INCOGNITA; a True account of Alchemical Plants & Sea Beasts & things of Greate Otherness.

Discovered Journals of Roote Gatherers aboard the doomed expedition of the Neptune who encountered, seeking The Garden of Cyrus, That *terrible, boundless* Element, the *North,*

became his Prisoner ; perished in the Cause of Science

lost on the yce & looking always
for the mysticall hid thing
that hath a misterie
deep in it
1644

Compiled, corrected & *now published in English.*

ab Aquilono omne malum

The wind has been in our teeth since the 15th
and myself too sick to write.

Never knew that salte could freese
tears so huge as to break a ship.

Calm in the evening: Sea covered with a pellicle of ice.

Second mate opened his mouth
thinking the waves had been white Swannes

                    ; ambiguous paradise.

Trimmed in yce :
there was a map
I carried it.

Raised
emblems

of men adrift.

*What can
be said
of the
smallest
degree.*

Having neither a chronometer nor the means of taking a lunar
observation; we set out ignorant of the meridian on which we sailed.

          One ship of the line : way out.

At mid-night the Sun
was seen above the horizon.
The eyes of men ache & twist : are marigolds.

*We have
had no
appearance
of Night
for this ten
days.*

Looking starboard in frangible snow, glimpsed—
as lively a red
as any that are in our gardens.

*Unaccountable
Roses
(on the
shores of ice
floes)*

I prayed to keep the plaits of thorns
alive while I was blinking. Ralph assured me

he would go stark mad if the excitement didn't stop soon.

The coast at night : teeming with sea spiders,
luminous green insects—
of the latter many millions.
I prepared the Righteous Foundation of the World
cupping a crisp bubble of seaweed out of the surf.

Every minute
I would like to be :

more innocent.

A Suckling whale found; swoln
in a fog of gulls— The sea that grazed its tail was turbid
olive green. We entangled it.

The Mother scoured the adjacent Sea
with great alarm and resolution,
she hurries onwards round the object of her care
daring to rise even amidst the watchful boats.

Thus she is snared to her affection

*Maternal
affection of
the whale A
Mother will
not desert
her
offspring
while life
remains in
it or
herself.*

Sat on the peak of an ice-mountain:
I saw the West with poppyheads
attended by the Evening Star; nightless
sleeping: It was so narrow that I sat across it as on Horseback.

One of four tents
on the tundra, he oversleeps in a blubber cask
and wakes between a footprint

and an iceberg.

Whispered as we went: *It is here that the hurt is
in the same Place there grows a cure.*

I saw him Mortifie & turne to frost inside my astrolabe.

Some were for remaining
by the ice. But the ice afforded no shelter.

Frozen stiff, stark dead
beneath the Greater Bear and in its winds

sitting as though alive & guiding
their horses who guided themselves
among the tents : the most returned.

*The Captain:
He was
become
another
Columbus
so also nowe
by conquest
he woold
become
another
Cortes.*

Cold makes wolves
fiercer to all animals
& also to each other.
Makes all seeds
sown
    Cold breaks stones
in the field

    & makes wars to take
place on frozen water.
Cold makes the wild
beasts seek out men's
dwellings

their pelts made thicker
& handsomer by cold.

∧∧ ∧ ∧∧∧ ∧∧ ∧ ∧
Ten peaks
cloud-hidden in ocean.

The Wreck of the *Annabelle Lee*

Robert Walton

Gaslight burst bright from crystal chandeliers and turned linen tablecloths to fields of snow. Joaquín Murrieta and Captain George Dutton sat in convivial silence with snifters of brandy before them.

Dutton laughed and lowered his newspaper. "This ad in today's *Chronicle* may interest you."

Joaquín turned. "Indeed?"

"It says that you may pay a nickel to view the head of the infamous bandit, Joaquín Murrieta!"

"I may look in any mirror and view that head without cost."

"It is undoubtedly in better condition than the one they're exhibiting in a jar down by the docks."

Joaquín didn't answer.

Dutton studied the ad. "Bah! Harry Love made thousands off of that head. Collecting the reward for killing you was the greatest fraud in the history of California."

"Well, he did kill someone."

"Obviously." Dutton removed a cigar from his vest pocket, trimmed its end with his penknife, and placed it between his lips. A waiter appeared and offered him a light. Dutton puffed several times, then leaned back in his chair. The waiter returned to attentive shadows.

Joaquín raised his glass and breathed in fragrant fumes. "Ah, Napoleon. The perfect end to a perfect meal."

Dutton nodded affably. "You approve of the Men's Grill Room, then?"

"How could I not? Even London would find it difficult to match this hotel."

"The Palace is a fine establishment, a great San Francisco institution, no doubt."

Joaquín smiled. "No doubt."

"I'm glad you're free to sail to Los Angeles with me. My business will take but a day. Perhaps we can return by land, and you can be a guest at my hotel in Jolon?"

Joaquín nodded. "Perhaps."

An exceedingly tall, clean-shaven, young man entered the dining room, and Dutton gestured to him with his cigar. "Ah, Mr. William Randolph Hearst. His father is a U.S. Senator. He will journey south with us."

Joaquín glanced at Hearst. "Perhaps Mr. Hearst will join us for brandy?"

Dutton shook his head. "No, no, he is a teetotaler. Rumor has it that he would like to become a mover and shaker in California."

"How so?"

"He intends to become a newspaper man. I've heard he is interested in taking control of the *Examiner*."

Joaquín shrugged. "There are many newspapers in San Francisco."

"Yes, many. He's also a neighbor of mine." Dutton raised his hand in greeting.

Hearst approached their table. Both Dutton and Joaquín stood.

"Mr. Hearst," Dutton said, "allow me to introduce you to my friend, Joaquín Murrieta."

Hearst's eyes widened. He extended his hand to Joaquín, and Joaquín took it. Hearst said, "Mr. Murrieta, I'm delighted to meet you."

Joaquín bowed slightly. "And I you."

"Your reputation precedes you, and accounts of your adventures never fail to astound me."

Joaquín shrugged. "Astound is a strong word."

Hearst smiled. "Though appropriate, I think. Wild, savage tales swirl about you; yet, you are a gentleman."

Joaquín shrugged again. "People exaggerate."

"I have a previous engagement," Hearst said, "but I understand that we will be sailing together tomorrow. I look forward to conversing with you further, Mr. Murrieta."

"The pleasure will be mine," Joaquín said.

Hearst turned and walked out of the grill's far exit. Joaquín and Dutton seated themselves. Dutton puffed his cigar. Joaquín sipped his brandy.

Dutton gestured with his cigar. "He's right, you know."

"What?"

"The stories don't match the civilized man sipping brandy across from me."

Joaquín grimaced. "I can do nothing about stories."

Dutton shook his head. "Still, something has changed you, calmed you, Mr. Murrieta. What?"

"Age."

Dutton studied his cigar. "Age and its wisdom?"

Joaquín smiled. "Just age."

•

Joaquín and Dutton stood together on the *Annabelle Lee*'s upper deck. Joaquín breathed sea air deep into his lungs and sighed with satisfaction at the leisure promised by this unexpected voyage.

"She's not an especially fast steamer," Dutton said, "but we've passed through the Golden Gate already."

"A bridge will span that entrance someday."

"Bah! You're a dreamer, my friend," Dutton said. "The distance between the headlands is more than two miles. Impossible!"

"You underestimate human ingenuity."

"You overestimate human capacity." Dutton pulled up his coat collar. "I'm going below. Too chilly up here."

Joaquín pulled his coat tighter, but remained leaning on the port rail, watching verdant coastal hills sweep by. A slight movement, a flicker of orange, caught his eye by the corner of the pilothouse. A small Chinese man in his middle years sat cross-legged with his back against the rear pilothouse wall. He bent studiously over a notebook, his stub of pencil moving swiftly.

Curious, Joaquín approached him. The man looked up as Joaquín came even with him. Their eyes met, and the man hastily shut his notebook. Joaquín glimpsed a string of figures and equations before the book's worn, red covers slapped shut.

"Mathematics?" Joaquín asked. "Perhaps geometry?"

"Spherical trigonometry. It is a hobby, sir. I often have time between my various duties, you see. Mathematics harms nothing and occupies my mind."

A woman spoke from behind Joaquín, "Perhaps your mind should be occupied with reserving our table for dinner, Wong?"

Joaquín turned. A beautiful woman smiled at him. She was perhaps forty, expensively dressed in a burgundy dress with matching short jacket and hat. Her blouse was of creamy silk, and she wore silken gloves. Gold gleamed at her throat and upon her wrists and fingers.

Wong rose and bowed. "As you wish, ma'am." He stuffed the notebook in his pocket, bowed again, and made his way toward the main salon.

The woman said, "I don't believe we've met. I'm Molly Maguire."

"Joaquín Murrieta," he nodded, "at your service."

"Please excuse Wong, Mr. Murrieta. He is my servant, and I apologize if he was impertinent."

"Not at all. He was most polite. Are you dining now?" He offered Molly his arm.

She patted his sleeve. "Why, thank you, sir." She tucked his arm close to her side and stepped through the swinging doors to the ship's salon.

Joaquín glanced sideways at her. "Your pendant is very beautiful."

"You're too kind." The brightly lit salon became measurably brighter by her smile. "It is an attractive piece, perhaps a trifle gaudy, but of little value."

"Might I inquire what the stone is?"

"Certainly. It's olivine, semi-precious but not at all rare."

He looked at the sea-green, translucent stone. Darker inclusions swirled in graceful patterns at its heart. The two reached a table near the center of the room.

Molly halted. "Thank you very much, Mr. Murrieta. Won't you join me for dinner?"

"Alas, I have a prior arrangement." He bowed. "If you will excuse me?"

She smiled and released his arm. "Of course. Perhaps another time?"

"I would be most pleased."

•

After dinner, Hearst, Dutton, and Joaquín stood at the ship's rail studying the bleak coast south of San Francisco. Joaquín and Dutton enjoyed their cigars while Hearst tapped his fingers upon the rail.

Dutton said to Joaquín, "Did you notice the bald fellow several tables away from us?"

Joaquín nodded.

"That's Morgan Bernard."

"The Virginia City miner?"

Hearst shook his head. "Not a miner, Mr. Murrieta. Mr. Bernard was in transportation and supply. That's where real money is. He was the only game in town for some years. Profit margins of several hundred percent were the norm on all articles."

"And now?"

"He has competition now."

Joaquín nodded. "So, he finds other business?"

Hearst's fingers tapped more swiftly. "Mr. Bernard doesn't like competition. Businesspeople have arrived in Virginia City who won't be bullied, cheated, or burned out. I believe Mr. Bernard means to travel east."

Joaquín looked at Hearst. "Wealthy?"

Dutton laughed. "Shamefully."

Hearst said, "There is nothing shameful about wealth, Captain, nothing at all."

Dutton shrugged. "It's rumored that he carries much of his fortune with him on this ship."

Hearst nodded. "Diamonds, specie, gold bonds, and cash: all in the purser's safe."

Joaquín asked, "Millions?"

"At least," Dutton snorted.

Joaquín puffed on his cigar. "That is good. I am invited to join him at poker this evening."

•

Joaquín's fingers rested on the green baize of the card table. He paused for a moment before he raised the edge of the newly dealt card before him. It was his last hole card, a ten. It joined another ten and a jack, his first two hole cards. A third ten and a second jack lay face up on the table. He had a full house, quite a good full house. Face still as a twilight pond, he studied the card as if trying to decipher its markings. At last, he lowered it and looked up. Morgan Bernard stared at him. There was a gleam of expectation in the man's eye. In an honest game, this was a hand on which to bet a small fortune.

Joaquín smiled and murmured, "I fold."

Bernard's eyebrows shot up. "What did you say?"

Joaquín locked eyes with Bernard. "I did not get my card. I fold." Joaquín had not spotted the card manipulation, but he had no doubt that one had occurred.

Bernard looked away. "Then the pot is mine." He reached with both hands to sweep the pile of chips, gold coins, and bills from the center of the table.

54

Molly said, "Excuse me, Mr. Bernard. I have yet to bet."

Bernard's hands froze in place, and he looked at her. "You intend to bet, Madame?"

Molly nodded primly. "I'm considering it."

Bernard leaned back, folded his hands, and snorted. "Well, get on with it, woman. We haven't got all night."

Molly smiled shyly. "Well, I should like to make a raise of $25,000."

Gasps sounded around the table. The wider room went silent.

The dealer swallowed and said, "I'm sorry, ma'am, but the custom on this ship is to accept table stakes only. Have you got $25,000?"

She plopped the wads of cash on the table in front of her cards. "Right here," she answered sweetly.

Bernard rubbed his chin, then said, "I'll call that bet." He looked at the dealer. "My cash is in the purser's safe. I'm sure you'll waive custom this one time, won't you?"

The dealer paused, then said, "Yes, sir."

Bernard looked at Molly and smiled. One at a time, he exposed three kings and two aces. He again reached for the pot.

Molly said, "Mr. Bernard, where are your manners? At least let me show you my hand. I have two of these." She turned a hole-queen and placed it next to an up-queen. "And two more of these." She turned over the last two queens.

A shock fell over the table like a rock into a green pond. Ripples of silence spread into the room beyond.

Molly sparkled. "Oh, my! I believe that's the winning hand."

Bernard's face turned red, and the flush rose across his bald scalp. He surged to his feet. His chair fell backward with a crash. "That's impossible!"

"Well, Mr. Bernard, four queens are there for all to see." Her impervious smile silenced Bernard's curse before it reached his lips. She said, "Wong, would you gather these for me?" Wong reached down and pulled the chips and money toward a silk bag he'd produced from his jacket pocket. "Now, as for the remainder, Mr. Bernard, might we meet in the purser's office in half an hour or so? I need to freshen up first, but I believe in completing transactions of this nature promptly."

Bernard snarled something indecipherable and stalked toward the bar.

Molly looked at Joaquín. Her eyes twinkled. "Poor man! I think he bet more than he could afford to lose."

•

Second Lieutenant Thaddeus Pearson peered nervously out of the bridge windows. Flags of fog streamed back from the bow. He glanced at the compass heading. It was steady and correct. He gazed out at the fog. The *Annabelle Lee* was proceeding at a cautious seven knots. He wondered if he should reduce speed further.

The fog dispersed suddenly. Surf-fringed rocks appeared dead ahead. Pearson gaped with dawning horror.

•

Bernard handed Molly a neatly tied bundle of bills. His face was flushed, but he spoke calmly. "I should like a chance to retrieve my losses. Perhaps tomorrow night?"

Molly smiled. "Perhaps."

She glanced at the clock on the bulkhead above the purser's desk, at the open door of the safe, and then at the purser. He nodded. She raised an eyebrow to Wong who stood behind Bernard. Wong also nodded.

•

The *Annabelle Lee* crashed hard on a submerged horn of rock and rode up onto it before stopping. Screams and subsidiary crashes sounded in the distance. Pearson picked himself up from the tilted deck. He leaned against the compass binnacle and stared wildly from left to right. Sweat started from his brow.

He shouted, "What happened?"

Helmsman Jenkins said, "We're hard aground, sir."

Pearson said, "Helm amidships. Engines back full."

"Belay that!" Captain Troop spoke from the rear of the bridge. His voice was quiet but firm. He stepped close to Pearson and muttered, "That reef is the only thing keeping us afloat. We'll be on the bottom in under three minutes if we slip off."

Pearson gulped. "Yes, sir."

Troop looked at the helmsman. "Jenkins, keep that helm amidships."

"Aye, aye, sir."

Troop stepped to the engine room voice pipe. "Engine room?"

"Engine room here, Captain."

Troop spoke slowly, "I'm going to ring for dead slow in a moment. I want it slower than that, just a few turns of the screw to keep us in place. Got that, Scottie?"

"Aye, Captain."

"Pearson?"

"Sir?"

"That's Pedernales Point off the port bow."

"Yes, Captain."

"Do you have any idea why it's there?"

Pearson swallowed. "I don't know, Captain. We followed the compass heading as ordered. I was about to reduce speed, when we came out of the fog, and there it was."

Captain Troop stood silent for a moment before he spoke again. "It's a calm night. We should be able to save everyone. The ship is another matter. We'll need help and luck for that. Have all passengers board the lifeboats. It will take two trips to get everyone on shore. Women and children first."

"Aye, sir."

Troop turned to Pearson. His gaze was icy, though fierce. "I'm going below to inspect our damage. Do not move this ship! Is that clear?"

"Yes, sir."

Bonfire flames rose twelve feet in the air and bent east with a breeze from the nearby fog. Sands glowed orange for many yards to either side of them. Frightened faces stared out at the motionless *Annabelle Lee*, still pinned upon the hidden rock, small waves sucking at her flanks. Some of the younger passengers threw driftwood logs on the fire.

Seven lifeboats lined the shore. An eighth pulled in at the end of the line and drove hard into the sand. Two sailors leapt into the water, ran up the beach with a rope, and secured it to a redwood log.

Captain Dutton climbed over a gunwale and stepped into knee-deep water. He snorted with disgust. "These were new boots!"

Grinning, Joaquín joined him. "Not to worry, my friend. I suspect that the shipping company will reimburse you."

"Bah!"

"Shall we help the lady?"

"What lady?"

Molly's face glowed golden in the light of the giant fire. "Gentlemen, a hand, if you please?"

Dutton and Joaquín lifted her clear of the gunwale, past the slapping water, and onto dry sand.

"Thank you."

Joaquín bowed. "It was our pleasure."

Molly smiled. "I think I shall step closer to the fire."

"An excellent idea!"

Molly walked away from them. Both men watched her move among the bedraggled passengers, offering a cheery word here and a helpful suggestion there.

Dutton rubbed his chin. "I thought they said 'women and children first.'"

A splash sounded behind them. They turned and saw Wong standing in the water. He was holding two of Molly's suitcases. Eyes down, he bowed his head to them and walked onto the beach after Molly.

Dutton eyed the heavy suitcases. "It's a good thing the Pacific lived up to its name tonight. He never would have gotten ashore carrying those two bags otherwise."

Joaquín nodded.

Lieutenant Pearson joined Joaquín and Dutton. "Well, that's it. All the passengers are safe."

"What of Captain Troop?" Joaquín looked at the distant *Annabelle Lee*.

"He'll stay aboard with a skeleton crew. He thinks that a patch can be fashioned and that the ship can be saved, especially if a tug arrives before the seas pick up."

Dutton looked at him. "What if he's wrong?"

"They still have the jolly boat, sir."

"Lieutenant," Joaquín asked, "was our boat the last carrying passengers?"

"Yes, sir."

"Mrs. Maguire was with us."

Pearson nodded. "I thought all the women and children were evacuated on the first trips to shore, but she popped out of the shadows with her man just as we were loading this last trip. I believe you and Captain Dutton were already in the lifeboat. I can't imagine why she waited."

"I see. It's not important." He watched Molly move among the slowly relaxing passengers. "Do you have further duties, Lieutenant?"

"Just to make the passengers as comfortable as possible until help arrives."

"Captain Dutton and I will assist you as we can."

"Thank you, sir."

Dutton looked down at his soggy boots. "Shall we step closer to the fire?"

Joaquín clapped him on the back. "A fine idea, my friend. It is a true beacon, and I can feel its heat from here."

The three men moved into ruddy light. The red fire offered defiance to night and sea. The *Annabelle Lee*'s passengers, exhausted and chilled, huddled within its comforting circle of warmth as dawn eased into the eastern sky.

•

A battered cab rolled to a halt within the cavernous Grand Court of the Palace Hotel. Captain Dutton waited as the cabbie secured his reins, climbed down from the box, and opened the cab door. Joaquín stepped out. He paid the cabbie with silver coins and turned to Dutton.

Dutton extended his hand. "We meet again."

Joaquín smiled and took it. "And again in the Palace Hotel."

"Your trip from Los Angeles was uneventful?"

"Tedious is a better word."

"Your tedium is at an end." Dutton indicated the vast space in which they stood. "The magnificence of these colonnades, however, always makes me feel that my business here, whatever it is, should be more important."

Joaquín laughed. "Even the idle musings of a man of substance are more important than any tower of colonnades. You, sir, are a man of substance."

Dutton bowed. "If you say so, my friend. Shall we adjourn within?"

A second cab pulled up as the first made its slow turn toward the exit. The cabbie opened the door and offered his hand to a lady. The lady stepped out. It was Molly Maguire.

Dutton narrowed his eyes. "Chance meetings with old acquaintances."

Joaquín said, "Not so strange, I think. She may have been on the same train I took from Los Angeles. Our meeting is fated, perhaps. I believe I have something that belongs to her."

Dutton glanced at Joaquín. "Really?"

Joaquín stepped toward Molly.

She saw him and smiled. "Mr. Murrieta! What a pleasant surprise!"

Joaquín bowed. "Fate has many surprises, some pleasant. Our recent voyage had a surprising termination, no?"

Molly nodded. "It did, indeed, though the ship was not lost."

Dutton said, "We had a skillful captain."

"And it was a calm night for small boat landings upon a deserted shore," continued Joaquín.

Molly smiled. "We were most fortunate."

Joaquín said, "Except for Mr. Bernard. He claimed to have lost more than $300,000 in gold bonds from the purser's safe."

Molly shrugged. "That unpleasant man! He should count his blessings! He was injured in the crash, you know. Hit his head badly. We had quite a struggle dragging him to a boat. He's not a light man. The safe, I suppose, was left open. Some crewman must have removed those bonds in the confusion of the wreck. I understand that most of his treasure was saved, however."

Joaquín nodded. "I believe so."

"You have experience with robbers, do you not?"

"I do."

"Don't you find that greed most often defeats them?"

Joaquín nodded. "It can."

"Well," Molly said, "if there were a thief, he left Mr. Bernard's extremely valuable diamonds unmolested, no?"

He grinned. "It was a good night for saving jewelry." He pulled Molly's unique pendant from his vest pocket. "I believe this belongs to you."

Her eyes flickered with surprise. "Why, Mr. Murrieta, that's my pendant! Wherever did you find it?"

"I found it hanging from the compass binnacle on the bridge of the *Annabelle Lee*."

She took the pendant. "Truly?"

"Truly. I wonder how it might have gotten there?"

She laughed, a melodious sound in that hall of marble and horses. "Ah, a mystery! Perhaps we can discuss it at greater length after I'm checked in. Will you join me for luncheon in an hour? The Ladies' Grill Room, perhaps?"

Both men bowed. Dutton said, "We'd be delighted."

Molly, parasol aloft, swept into the hotel lobby under full sail.

Joaquín watched her. "I wonder where her Chinese servant is?"

Dutton shrugged. "Around back with the luggage, most likely. Guests of the Palace don't take their bags through the front door."

Joaquín, still staring at the entrance, said, "I wonder."

Dutton looked at him. "By the by, what were you doing on the bridge after we crashed?"

"Looking for a lady's necklace."

Dutton examined Joaquín closely. "Looking for it?"

"Yes, the gemstone is olivine."

"Olivine?"

"A combination of peridot and magnetite. Magnetite is, of course, a magnetic mineral strong enough to affect a compass."

"You don't say."

Joaquín smiled. "I do. Further, Mr. Wong is, or was, an exceptional servant. He is an accomplished mathematician and is especially adept at spherical trigonometry."

Dutton rubbed his chin. "That's a useful skill for an artilleryman."

"And also for a navigator, a very precise navigator."

"By God, Murrieta, what are you suggesting?"

"Nothing at all, Captain!"

"But you implied. . . ."

"No, no, I implied nothing! A crewmember must have found the pendant, perhaps the same one who took Bernard's bonds."

Dutton shook his head. "Damned strange coincidence, nonetheless."

Joaquín glanced up at the tiers of the marble colonnades rising ninety feet above their heads and changed the subject. "Magnificent! Still, California is subject to earthquakes, you know. I should not like to be standing here if one struck."

Dutton snorted. "Bah! These colonnades are solid! An earthquake couldn't even make them quiver."

Joaquín smiled but made no reply.

Dutton said, "The lady will require at least an hour to refresh herself before luncheon, likely more. Shall we repair to the bar?"

Joaquín nodded. "After you."

William Randolph Hearst, c. 1905.

Harry Love, the lawman who allegedly killed Murrieta and displayed the bandit's head in a sideshow, 1850s.

THE HEAD

OF THE RENOWNED BANDIT

JOAQUIN!

TO BE EXHIBITED

AT THE
STOCKTON HOUSE

AUG. 19, 1853 – $1

ONE DAY ONLY

Exhibition poster, 1853.

The following is one of the many affidavits, certificates, &c., proving the identity of the Head:

STATE OF CALIFORNIA—COUNTY OF SAN FRANCISCO, ss : Ignacio Lisarraga, of Sonora, being duly sworn, says :– That he has seen the alleged head of Joaquin, now on exhibition and That deponent was well acquainted with Joaquin Murrieta, and that the head exhibited as above is and was the veritable head of Joaquin Murrieta, the celebrated Bandit. And further says not. IGNACIO LISARRAGA.

Joaquín Murrieta, c. 1853.

61

July Haiku

L. Shapley Bassen

The New York Times *article,*
p. A24, July 15, 2010, David W. Dunlap

1
Aft of vessel from
the 18th century found
beneath Ground Zero.

2
Newton did not know
the speed of light, nor Shakespeare
imagine us now.

Sir Isaac Newton, 1689.

Sonnet LXXX (80)

William Shakespeare

written in 1609

O! how I faint when I of you do write,
Knowing a better spirit doth use your name,
And in the praise thereof spends all his might,
To make me tongue-tied speaking of your fame.
But since your worth, wide as the ocean is,
The humble as the proudest sail doth bear,
My saucy bark, inferior far to his,
On your broad main doth willfully appear.
Your shallowest help will hold me up afloat,
Whilst he upon your soundless deep doth ride;
Or, being wracked, I am a worthless boat,
He of tall building, and of goodly pride:
   Then if he thrive and I be cast away,
   The worst was this, my love was my decay.

William Shakespeare, c. 1600.
Engraving by William Holl, c. 1820s.

A Lighterman's Tale

Mike Fox

It was my fate to be a lighterman, as it is the fate of most every son of a lighterman. The old men say the rhythms of the tide—swell to the west, ebb to the east—are born with you, as the blood flows in your veins. In truth, we are creatures of the water and find our peace there, cruel though it can be.

Now, I suppose, I am one of those old men: a "Freeman of the River Thames," the master of forty miles of tideway. I've known that stretch of water through long hours of day and night, in all seasons and every mood of weather. I have been pilot to both barge and cargo, with only twenty-five feet of cheap Swedish deal and the will of the tide to steer by. Yet, my work has been my consolation and freedom, and a rare kind of freedom it has been.

But at the time I will speak of, that freedom had still to be won. I was bound in the servitude of an apprenticeship, though I had gained my license and could take a barge out on my own. Those early days, before I achieved full instinct, could be hazardous, especially when the river was crowded with other vessels. One false maneuver or error of judgment and your guvnor could put you out on your neck, providing you survived to give him opportunity.

Because the Thames is a fine lady, and strong enough to carry all the freight of London. But she has her moods, and she has her feelings. To keep her favor, you must learn these and obey them. Fanciful though it sounds, I believe this understanding prepared me, as best anything could, for what I will now describe.

It was a fair morning in early May, and I was dropping down the river on the tide. The whistle came not from the water but far to my left, from the bank. It was *our* whistle, the whistle of our company: taken in another century from the song of a thrush. I looked towards it expecting to see a workmate, and there she stood, a girl as beautiful as I could ever imagine, with two fingers stuck in her mouth and bent almost double to prise the noise from her lungs.

All I could think to do was reply in kind, as no voice would carry across that stretch of water. So, I pressed my lips wide in similar fashion and blew as hard as I could, which almost cost me the grip of my oar. In all, it must have been an ungainly gesture, and I could see her wiping tears of laughter from her eyes as the tide bore me away.

To this day, I do not know how this small circumstance became common knowledge, except to say there is little privacy on a commercial river. I will also never know if my guvnor caught word and, for his own reasons, took the action he did.

"I want you to walk yourself up to Clerkenwell and collect six pair of strap hinges from Eagan's," he said, the following morning as I entered his office to learn my duties for the day. "I ordered them last week, so they know what to give you, and all you have to do is sign the firm's account." He said this barely looking up at me.

"I'll go straight away, Guvnor," I said, careful of my delight. A three-mile stroll on a warm spring day was not the worst thing he could have asked me to do.

So, I stepped away northward with a light heart. Eagan's Ironmongery was a magical place, with drawers from floor to ceiling holding every type of device and contraption you could dream of, and tradesmen from all around the city made their way there.

When I arrived, as I foresaw, there was a queue. What I did not foresee was the vision stood facing that queue from behind the counter. Because it was the girl from the riverbank, in a brown warehouse coat with the sleeves rolled up, serving the rough men with a smile and full confidence in herself.

The queue lent me time to gaze at her, and my eyes could go nowhere else. Her hair, full of curls, shone like the sun on fresh copper, and she looked slender and neat, even in that brown coat. Perhaps five minutes passed until I stood before her.

"How may I help you, sir?" she said, as she had to each man before me. And yet there was a tease in her smile that I believe none of them had witnessed.

"I've come for six pair of strap hinges for Slater's," I said. "My guvnor says he ordered them and asks they be added to his account."

"I have them here and ready," she said, reaching under the counter, which took me aback for a moment. She wrapped them in thick, brown paper and tied them neatly with string, all the while with an air about her I have no words for. Then, placing carbon paper between the pages, she filled out the invoice book in a careful hand.

"Could I have your signature here, sir," she said, holding my eye again.

"You were whistling to me on the river," I found myself blurting out.

"I might have been," she said, as if using me for her amusement.

"But my company's whistle's a secret."

"Not to me it isn't," she said, tilting her chin forward so that I noticed it had a dimple.

Now, as a bound apprentice I was allowed neither marriage nor fornication, though the latter would have been very hard to come by anyway, especially as most of my strength was saved for the river. But a chance like this I knew might never fall my way again.

"Would you walk out with me on Sunday afternoon?" I said, risking the jeers of the men queuing behind me. "We could go by Spitalfields for pie and mash."

"You must ask permission of my uncle." She spent a moment clearing the invoice book away. "But if he agrees, I've no objection."

"And where would I find him?" I asked.

"If you stand aside while I serve these last three gentlemen, I'll go and fetch him." She smiled at me amusedly, then gave her attention to the next customer.

Now, I knew my guvnor would have a lively sense of how long an errand like this should take, but that was a risk I was willing to run. So, I stood aside, clutching the parcel and wondering quite what turn the day had taken.

When the customers had been served, she left the counter and passed through the open door in the corner, and I could hear her running up uncarpeted stairs, then after a moment a heavier tread coming down again. A thick-set man with receding hair and a brush of a mustache appeared through the door and placed his hands on the counter. The girl, his niece, stood behind him with her arms folded, observing us lightly.

"I understand you're Joe Cropper's youngest boy?" he said.

"I am, sir," I said, wondering how he knew this. He took a moment to run his eye over me.

"Your father and his forebears have been Thames lightermen for as long as anyone in this city can remember, and, if I'm fair, you look as steady as any of them I've come across."

"Thank you, sir," I said. "I intend to follow in their path to the best of my ability."

"Now, our Queenie tells me you hope to walk out with her," he continued, and I blessed him, as I realized I hadn't thought to ask her name.

"Yes, sir, that would be my hope," I said, standing as straight as I could.

"Well, so would many others, I can assure you, but you seem a polite young man, and your family stand you in good stead. I expect I shall see your father in the Red Lion before the week's end, and if he raises no objection, neither shall I. You may call for Queenie on Sunday at twelve midday, providing you get the go-ahead from your old man."

"Thank you, sir," I said again, and lifting my cap to them both, I left the shop to make my way back. I walked away on feet like feathers, and upon reaching the yard, passed the hinges to my guvnor, who made no comment other than to bid me steer some pig iron down to Limehouse.

I needn't tell you that, for the next few days, I waited on my father with the greatest attention at every moment we were at home together. He was with a different firm at that time, and some weeks, if our hours dictated, we might barely see each other at all. But that week he seemed to be home whenever I was, and I watched him like a dog observes meat on a bone.

Finally, on Friday, when overtime brought us fish and chips, he raised the matter. We were sat at the table with my mother and both brothers.

"John Eagan has spoken to me about his niece," he said, chewing unhurriedly. "It seems, for reasons only she can know, she's set her cap at you."

My brothers hooted in derision, and I did my best to kick their shins.

"Shut your cakehole, both of you," my mother came in. "Queenie Eagan is a most respectable girl, and it seems she's seen some merit in our Tom."

Everybody appeared to be in on the matter except me.

"What do you know of her?" I asked. "I've only met her the once—to talk to, anyhow."

"She was born just after you were," my mother said, "but her mother died giving birth to her, and her father drowned shortly thereafter, poor girl."

"Was her dad a lighterman?" my brother, Harry, asked.

"Yes, he was," said my father, "and a good one, too. But when they pulled him from the water down by Wapping, they found a flask of whisky almost empty in his pocket. The coroner said the loss of his wife must have unhinged him, as he'd always been known as a sober man."

"Then what happened to Queenie," I said, "and why haven't I come across her before?"

"She was passed 'round her uncles south of the river," Mum said, "but she did so well at school that John Eagan wanted her in his shop. She's been there for a good six months now."

Before I could put all this together in my mind, Dad came in again.

"Now, listen," he said. "John Eagan likes the look of you, and you won't get a better chance than this in your life, so I'll not stand in your way. But don't forget that an apprentice is judged by his conduct on land as well as on water. Woe betide you if you play fast and loose with that girl."

"I've no intention of playing fast and loose," I said, wondering if any romance had ever started in this fashion.

"Well, I'm glad to hear it," Dad said. "Just make sure you don't."

So, as a result of this conversation, it's fair to say that when I knocked at the side door of Eagan's at twelve sharp on Sunday, I was even more nervous than I might otherwise have been. My mother had ironed my shirt and trousers, and I'd rubbed fresh dubbin into my boots.

After only a few seconds, Queenie appeared at the door, smiling and cheery, and stepped out to join me in the street. I must confess the look of her almost took my breath from me. She wore a dark-green dress like a tunic, stopping just below her knee, with a gray cardigan to cover her shoulders. Her hair was tied with a black ribbon so that the thick copper ringlets I remembered hung loosely down her back.

"Hello, Queenie," I said. "I'm very pleased we have the chance to get to know each other." I'd practiced this in front of the mirror at home, but it still came out ridiculous.

"Uncle doesn't want me back 'til four," she said, as natural as could be, "so we could have our dinner like you said, then walk by the river, providing you haven't seen enough of it."

I had the feeling, as before, that I was causing her some sort of amusement, but if so, I was glad. I couldn't help wondering how an orphan girl could have so much joy in her.

"How did you come to be on the river?" she asked, as we walked side by side. "Not every boy follows his father these days."

"My teacher said it was all I was fit for," I told her, hoping, I must be honest, that she would exclaim otherwise.

Instead she said, "That's not a nice thing to hear," and took my arm, making me feel a foot taller.

And that was the start of it. From then on, we walked out every Sunday, and any other time I could contrive. There was never really any question, I

67

think. We both knew that whatever days life should give us thereafter would be spent together.

But I had four years and three months still to serve in my apprenticeship, and young flesh is rarely patient. There was no private place we could go to, only shop doorways on damp or windy nights to express our passion. We were seen doing just that and reported, by whom I do not know, and I was called to explain myself before the beadle at Waterman's Hall. When you're courting, it can seem that all the eyes of London are upon you.

On the appointed day, my father came with me. He wore his suit and a dark tie and, apart from a ten-minute grilling which will stay with me to my grave, said nothing else to me beforehand. The hall was not such a grand building, really, but as we walked through the passage to the beadle's office, passing the old prints of sailing ships and river scenes, I felt the weight of all that history bearing down on me. I remembered my father's warning and feared my days on the river might be coming to a premature end. Worse still, I feared bringing disgrace upon Queenie, so I was willing to take whatever blame was coming. But as we stood before the semicircle of dignitaries—master lightermen, wharfingers, and puffed-up company men—Dad set about making a case for me, and I saw a side to him I'd never glimpsed before.

I should explain that these men setting out to judge me were of two distinct categories: those who had spent their lives on the river and gained mastery through the experience, and those who had taken themselves into offices and never been seen afloat. As Dad began speaking on my behalf, it was clear he held the respect of both.

"Gentlemen," he said, once the charge was laid out, "I understand why my son is here, and what you may have heard about him. I, myself, have warned him of the dangers of courtship for a young man bound in apprenticeship. But I would ask you to consider two things. Queenie Eagan is the child of seven generations of lightermen. As well, it's the way of nature that a girl who lost her father early in life should seek fresh comfort in a steady man, which is what I believe my boy will become. Now, I've questioned him closely, and I can assure you that, despite what you may have heard, there has been no true impropriety. They are just two young people tied fast in love."

The beadle nodded judiciously. "Then, are you asking us to dismiss the charge that he was behaving improperly in a public place, in such a way as to discredit our trade?" he said.

"No, sir, I'm asking you and the panel to consider the matter in a different light. Anyone can see that Queenie Eagan and my son are on the path to matrimony and that they are aching for each other. I'm asking for dispensation for my son to marry before the term of his apprenticeship ends. What could benefit our proud trade more than the union of two of the oldest families it contains?"

The panel looked at one another and muttered in low tones, then the beadle cleared his throat and said in his pompous voice, "We now request that you retire to the hallway while we consider the points you've raised."

Dad and I went out and sat side by side on an oak pew in that dark and formal corridor. We said nothing, but his words rang in my head, and I thought of him with new pride. After several minutes, we were called back in. The beadle looked at us gravely, stroking his gold chain.

"You've spoken well on your son's behalf, Joe," he said, "and our opinion is that you've made a fair case. We, too, believe it would serve no purpose for your Tom to be lost to our trade. We agree, as well, that poor Queenie Eagan deserves our compassion and that the union of your family and hers can only be a good thing. Because of this, we are willing to see the matter brought before us in that light, and grant permission for the two of them to marry before Tom's apprenticeship runs its course. In fact, in view of events, we suggest sooner rather than later." He brought down his gavel, and we were dismissed.

So, there it was—the miracle of my life. Within two months, we were married on a late-autumn day at St. Georges in the East, and Queenie and I moved into the tiny attic room, cleared and scrubbed for us by my mother.

Of course, there was no honeymoon, but on our wedding night, our longing was released, and I touched her as tenderly as my sore and callused hands allowed. No words can describe what passed between us then, except to say her flesh was as tender as mine was rough, and as she held me to her breast, I felt all the ache of labor drawn from my body.

It was strange at first to have her in the house each day, and my brothers found new manners when she joined us at the table. But she was an easy girl to be with, and her good spirits cheered everyone. She continued to serve in her uncle's shop, and we began saving for the time we could move out to somewhere of our own.

With this in mind, I set myself to work with new strength and seriousness. By now, I was agile and had learned to tread the slithering gunwales with toes turned in, taking pigeon steps for balance. This is how you can tell a lighterman on dry land, because the habit never leaves us. As well, I was developing a sense of the water and could steer confidently through a road of barges and estimate the drop of the tide wherever I was called upon to moor.

But one morning, before even the winter had set in, Queenie woke in discomfort and without her usual spark. When my mother put toast before her as we sat down for breakfast, she rose hurriedly from her chair and made straight for the outside privy, returning some minutes later, ashen and tearful.

"Take yourself back to bed, my girl," Mum said, "and I'll heat you up a brick to ease your tummy. We'll send word to your uncle that you won't be in today." When Queenie had left us, Mum said, "There's cause for joy for us now, though I doubt she'll be feeling very joyful for the next few weeks."

I went to work that morning with the blessing of new life before me and the step of a father-to-be.

The sickness ran its course, and by the turn of the year, Queenie blossomed, with a bloom on her skin and a mystery about her that even my brothers beheld in wonder. I felt I had all that any man could wish for, and no task the river threw at me seemed too great. In fact, I was often sent out when the weather conditions and value of cargo would normally point my guvnor towards an older man.

It was on such a day, with Queenie due at any time, that I took a half-load of grass seed on the short run from Wapping to Rotherhithe. Fog had come down, but I'd learned to use my ears as eyes and let the water hone my senses. And perhaps because of this, on a day like any other, I began to feel unease. I could put no reason to it, nor could I let myself be distracted, but despite the cocoon of mist and the river being quiet and gentle, something told me all was not well.

And so it proved. When I reached the dock, I was waved past the queue of craft waiting to unload, and men on the quayside shouted for my mooring rope.

"You get yourself home, boy, quick as you can. Your mother's sent for you." The speaker was a man known to me only by sight.

"What is it?" I said. "Why am I wanted?" It was the sort of question you ask when you fear you know the answer.

"You just get there as quick as you can," he replied. "Take a bus; don't walk it."

It was not within my power to wait for a bus, so I ran the two miles home. When I arrived, I found only my mother—my father and brothers being out at work.

"What's happened?" I said. "Why have you sent for me?"

My mother folded me in her arms, like she hadn't done for years. "Your Queenie's dead," she said in her gentlest voice. "The baby came, and there was nothing they could do."

I felt all strength leave my body. "Didn't anybody help her?" I said.

"Of course they did, dearie," Mother said. "The doctor came, and the midwife's still up there now, and they managed to save the baby. You're the father of a son."

"Let me see them," I said. I was choking with tears.

"The midwife doesn't want you up there, Tom," Mother said. "She said not to let you. They'll bring the baby to us when they're ready to."

I sat down while she boiled the kettle.

"Hot, sweet tea," she said, placing a mug beside me.

Before I could even think of bringing it to my lips, the midwife came down the stairs, and I found myself on my feet. She looked at me steadily.

"She's gone, dear," she said. "There was nothing we could do but save the baby."

"But wasn't she in pain?" I said. "Surely she called for me earlier?"

"There's nothing more you need to know, my child," she said. "If I told you anything else, it wouldn't help you."

So, there I found myself, with no answer to the questions of life and separate in my spirit to all around me. When I held my son, I felt the pulse of his mother in his tiny body and knew that one way or another, I would carry on. That evening, my father nodded to the others to leave us, and stood behind where I sat with his hand on my shoulder.

"Get back to your work as soon as you can, boy," he said. "No tide loses all its salt, however far it's come from the sea. A lighterman will always find comfort amongst his own."

So, I walked down to the river in the late evening and sat on a bench there in the quietest spot I could find. I looked out onto the Thames and saw my son as a man upon it, perhaps finding a mother in the swell and dip of the tide, as have many others. I watched the water flowing swiftly on the ebb as the river ran on past the docks, twisting and widening in the dusk towards the estuary beyond, where, like yesterday and tomorrow, it would yield its dark mouth to the sea.

Nocturne: Blue and Gold, painted by James Abbott McNeill Whistler in 1872, depicts a lighterman steering his craft beneath Old Battersea Bridge on the River Thames.

The Rum Barrel

Angela Raper

Caroline Sloo stood on the Beaufort pier and flipped a silk fan in front of her face with idle flicks of her wrist, trying to stir up an artificial breeze. The scent of rotting fish permeated the air, and not even waving her fan faster was enough to dispel the odor without the help of a breeze, but the ocean was subdued today. Timid waves lapped at the pier posts, and the squawks from seagulls wheeling overhead sounded muffled in the still, humid air. She was perspiring, even though she'd worn a lightweight muslin dress, the one Eleanor called her "sky dress" because it was the bright blue of a North Carolina summer sky. Tendrils of blond hair worked loose from her chignon beneath her wide-brimmed straw hat and clung limply to her damp neck.

Caroline watched sailors aboard the *Hopewell* and dockhands on the pier work together to secure the gangplank, and her stomach fluttered as the crew began unloading cargo. Sturdy, sunburned men hefted crates and rolled barrels, making the wood gangplank creak ominously beneath the weight of sugar, molasses, and rum from the West Indies. Caroline fixed her gaze at the top of the gangplank, waiting to see Eleanor's curls glinting like gold doubloons in the sun. Perhaps they had been bleached white in the Caribbean heat. Eleanor was forever forgetting to wear her straw hat, turning her hair lighter with each summer day.

John appeared at the gangplank, but Caroline looked past him, narrowing her eyes as she tried to find Eleanor, who was her father's shadow when he was home. Perhaps too much togetherness had created a breach between them? Or perhaps traveling didn't suit Eleanor as much as she thought it would? It was easy to romanticize a seafaring life when one didn't have to think about seasickness or weeks spent confined on a ship, eating hardtack and dried meat. Caroline's mother had described the hardships she'd suffered on her passage from England, but that had never deterred Eleanor, who put more stock in John's tales of swaying palm trees with wide fronds rustling in the breeze coming off turquoise water and of fields of sugar cane growing higher than John was tall.

John moved out of the way of two sailors who were rolling a large barrel, and then he followed them down the gangplank, his expression grim. These sailors handled the barrel with unusual care. The creaking of the ramp wasn't loud enough to drown out the sloshing sounds or a rhythmic bumping as if something was rolling and pitching inside the barrel. They stopped in front of Caroline and set the barrel upright with gentle hands, then tugged their forelocks to Caroline before turning away.

She took a step back as she stared at the barrel. John was keeping some rum for himself this time. That *had* to be the answer. It was the only answer. John touched the barrel, clenching the raised rim until his knuckles turned pale. When she looked at him at last, she almost didn't know him. His tanned skin was lined, and his face was gaunt. His eyes—green, like Eleanor's—had gone dull.

"I kept my promise," he said hoarsely, and Caroline took a hesitant step forward as she looked past him, desperately seeking a glimpse of Eleanor.

She remembered the day they set sail, remembered how she had fussed with the grosgrain ribbon that secured Eleanor's straw hat beneath her round chin. It had been easier to worry about Eleanor getting sunburned than to think about everything else that might happen while her daughter was out of her sight.

She had grabbed Eleanor's elbow and forced Eleanor to stand still while she wet her handkerchief with her tongue and scrubbed at a faint trace of dirt on the embroidered stomacher of Eleanor's navy-blue muslin dress. She hadn't wanted to let Eleanor go, and a dirty stomacher was as good an excuse as any.

"Promise you'll bring her home to me, John," she had said on that day. "No matter what happens, bring her home."

John was good at keeping his promises, like the one he'd made to forsake all others and keep only unto her, but he never kept them in the way she would prefer.

So here Eleanor was, brought home to her after all.

Caroline reached out but stopped short of touching the barrel and snatched her hand back. The air was so oppressive, she could only draw in short, shallow breaths, and she fanned herself harder to keep from swooning in the heat.

"Thank you," she said. It was the only response she could think of here on the pier with sailors and laborers all around, casting curious gazes at them and the barrel. Did they know what it contained? Could they guess? How long would it be before the men from the *Hopewell* spread the news of the strange interment?

Once the cargo had been unloaded from the *Hopewell* and prepared for transportation to a warehouse, John loaded the barrel in the back of a wagon along with his trunks. He held out his hand to help Caroline onto the wagon, and she forced herself to take it. The feel of his callused fingers was familiar but unwelcome, and she tugged her hand free as soon as she was on the seat.

"Was there nothing on board ship you could have used to fashion a coffin?" she asked once they were away from the dock.

"We were too far from port. It was this or burial at sea. I had no other options."

Caroline pressed her fists over her ears, muffling the sound of sloshing rum as the wagon wheels jounced over the cobblestone streets. They returned to the two-story house John had built on Front Street for her during the first year of their marriage. They had quarreled often back then because she wanted him to remain in Beaufort and work for her father, but he refused. For her, the West Indies was too far. For John, who had dreams of seeing India and China, it wasn't far enough. The house was a sop to make up for his continued absences. It was constructed out of Scotch heart pine held together with hand-hewn pegs and sturdy enough to withstand the hurricanes that threatened Beaufort during the summer and fall. A Bahaman-style double porch ran along the front of the whitewashed house. The door opened onto a long hall with two rooms on each side and a staircase leading up to the bedrooms at the end. Caroline used the first room on the right as her parlor because the windows were long and wide, offering a clear view of the inlet.

After he unloaded the barrel from the back of the wagon, John stood with his hand resting lightly atop it, and Caroline shuddered and glanced away. She didn't even want to look at the barrel, and she didn't understand how he could bear the feel of its splintery wood beneath his palm.

"Where shall I put it?" he asked.

Caroline wasn't certain how to answer. Under normal circumstances, the coffin would be in the parlor, but she couldn't imagine putting a barrel on display like that. Yet she couldn't put it out of sight like it was nothing more than a delivery of molasses, either.

At last, she said, "Take it to the parlor."

She made herself watch as John rolled the barrel into the parlor, and it sat on her colorful woven rug, a squat thing with dirt ingrained in its nicks and patches of rust on its iron bands. A pine coffin in the room would have been bad enough, but at least she could have arranged flowers on it, perhaps draped Eleanor's favorite blanket over it to soften the sharp edges. What could she do to alleviate the ugly harshness of the barrel?

"It was yellow fever." John sat down in his usual chair by the hearth, his gaze straying away from Caroline to the barrel.

Caroline took a seat in her rocking chair—a hand-carved gift from her father before Eleanor's birth—and folded her hands in her lap. "She took ill on the return trip?"

"Yes, she got to see the islands as she so longed to do," John said.

And it killed her, was what Caroline wanted to say, but she had always prided herself on being a good and dutiful wife even though their marriage had been one of necessity rather than choice, and pride kept her silent now.

"How long . . .?" She couldn't finish the question.

"The fever came on when we were less than a week out of port." John was looking at her, but his sea-green eyes were vacant as if his spirit were back on the *Hopewell* with Eleanor. "I thought perhaps it was little more than a summer fever because we were caught in the rain one day. There was talk of yellow fever in Port Royal, but there is *always* talk of yellow fever." The focus of his eyes sharpened on her. "I made poultices."

Caroline thought about Eleanor's sniffles and fevers, the scrapes and bruises and splinters she had tended on her own while he was away at sea. He didn't see Eleanor for the first time until she was over two months old, and by that time, Caroline had dealt with croup twice. "You made poultices."

"It was all I knew to do." His mouth formed a peevish moue. "We have

74

no doctor aboard ship. You know that. The carpenter only knows how to amputate limbs. He was of no use."

Apparently, neither were you. The words pushed against her lips, and she swallowed them with effort, their bitterness lingering on her tongue.

She stood and approached the barrel, pressing her palms against the folds of her skirt to keep them from brushing against it. How could they bury a barrel?

"I want a coffin," she said, pivoting sharply to face John. "A proper one. She deserves it."

"It's not practical," John said, watching her with his head tilted like an alert dog.

"I care nothing for *practical*." She wrinkled the muslin of her sky dress with the sweat of her palms as she fisted her hands in it. "I'll not have our child in a *barrel* until Judgment Day."

John rose to his feet. "Captain Hammond would have had her buried at sea, but I kept my promise to you. We were over a week from port. It was this way or naught. Would you prefer I had wrapped her in sailcloth and pitched her overboard like unwanted cargo?"

"I would prefer her not to be in a barrel."

"I'll not be the one who takes her out of it," John said. "Think on what is in that barrel, and tell me if you truly wish to exhume it."

Caroline sucked in a sharp breath as she thought about her daughter's body with its knees tucked under its chin, protected in its second womb. The body that had been teetering on the line between child and woman. She would have been tall and slender, like the Sloos. Like John. Eleanor had so much of him—his height, his eyes, his wanderlust—and so little of her. She had tried to prepare Eleanor for the role of wife and mother, but Eleanor was far more interested in studying maps than in learning how to bake bread or knit socks.

She thought about that body submerged in rum for so long, about bloated flesh falling off the bone and liquefied green eyes oozing out of their sockets.

"No," she whispered. "We shall bury the barrel."

She struggled to swallow the gulping sobs that rose in her throat. She couldn't stand being here any longer—couldn't stand looking at him or that barrel or all the little things around the house that evoked memories of Eleanor. Her favorite books on the shelf, the stool carved for her by Caroline's father, the misshapen and unfinished scarf in Caroline's work basket from Eleanor's failed attempt at knitting.

"I am going to my father's house," she said.

"You always do."

Once, she would have responded to the provocation, but today, she swept past him in silence and walked the two blocks to her parents' house. She wanted to tell them about Eleanor herself before the gossips got hold of the news; she wanted the comfort they would offer. Her father, Gideon, was still at his general store, but her mother, Nell, was in the small kitchen in the backyard, kneading bread in a wide bowl made of smooth, pale oak. When Nell looked up, she smiled a welcome that faltered as she gazed at

Caroline.

"Whatever is the matter?"

Caroline shook her head, not yet able to say the words that would make it all real. Nell held out her arms, and Caroline fell into the embrace, heedless of the flour on her mother's hands and clothes, and she wailed out her grief.

"My girl is dead," she said when she could speak at last.

Nell said nothing, only held Caroline tighter. Both of them had known the loss of a child. Caroline had borne four children, but Eleanor was the only one who survived infancy. Nell had borne six, three of whom lived to adulthood, but Caroline's older brother had died following an attack of apoplexy two years ago.

After Caroline's weeping abated, her mother sat her down by the iron stove and heated the kettle to make tea while Caroline told her what happened.

"What will you do now?"

"Bury the barrel."

"I mean after," Nell said.

Caroline watched her mother in silence. She couldn't think about anything but the barrel in her parlor, much less an *after*.

"You're welcome to come here, you know."

It wasn't the first time Nell had made the offer; she had never liked John's wandering ways. It was, however, the first time Caroline considered accepting it. Eleanor was the reason she had married John, although she fancied herself in love with him at the time. What was supposed to be a brief affair while he was in port had shackled them to each other for the next twelve years.

"I've lost my child, my heart, my very *life*," Caroline said, clenching her fingers on the saucer. "I'll not give up my house, as well."

"Nor should you have to," Nell said. "But losing a child is a hard burden to bear. You might want to live where her ghost doesn't walk."

"I might." Caroline inclined her head slightly and turned her gaze down to her teacup. "But it also might be a comfort to have her memory so near."

"You'll know soon enough."

When Caroline returned home, she stopped the clocks and draped all the mirrors with black crepe, and she sat with the barrel in the parlor. John holed up in the back room he used as his office, and she didn't bother to draw him out, relieved she didn't have to look at him.

Neighbors came to call the next day, bringing sympathy along with loaves of freshly baked bread, pewter plates loaded with thick slices of salt- and smoke-cured ham, and other dishes. Caroline wouldn't have to think about preparing any meals for the next few days. She invited them in, desperate for any distraction that would break the silence in her home, but they cut their eyes at the open parlor door and made their excuses. She wondered if a glance at the barrel was all they had really come for.

At suppertime, Caroline left the parlor and walked down the hall to John's office. The door was closed as it had been all day, and she paused, debating whether to ask if he wanted something to eat or to let him fend for himself. She was about to leave when muffled sobs reached her, audible in the stillness pervading the house. Her heart lurched, and she pressed her open palm against the door.

She almost spoke, almost opened the door, almost offered consolation. They should have sought comfort from each other, but a roil of anger and resentment churned in her stomach at the thought of assuaging his grief as a good wife should, and she turned away from the door.

"You *should* feel it—all of it," she whispered as she walked away.

That night, the other side of the bed they shared remained empty, which was no different from most nights of their married life. The next morning, John didn't say where he had slept, and she didn't ask, more relieved than concerned by his absence.

On the day of the burial, Caroline dressed in her black linen dress with a black petticoat, and she tied her straw hat under her chin with a black ribbon. John joined her in the parlor while they waited for the wagon that would carry the barrel to the churchyard. She wished now that she had cleaned off the embedded grime and polished away the rust. She fished out her handkerchief and ran it over the top of the barrel. Then she knelt and smoothed the cloth up and down the sides before resting her cheek against the slats and closing her eyes.

"I am sorry." John's thick voice made her open her eyes again, but she didn't draw back from the barrel.

"I care not." She wrapped her arms around the barrel as far as she could, but it was too wide for her to embrace completely. John gaped at her, but she couldn't bring herself to feel remorse for speaking so bluntly.

"I have traveled there and back again safely countless times. I thought this time would be no different," he said at last.

"Travel comes with great risk." Caroline rubbed her cheek against a cool band, the metallic tang of iron filling her nose. "You know that. She did not. Her head was full of the wondrous tales you spun instead of telling her the truth about storms that might wash her overboard and fevers that might burn her to a husk."

"I never wanted it to happen," John whispered, his face pale and stricken.

"But it *did* happen. Because you wanted her to be like you." Caroline stood up, steadying herself with a hand on the barrel. Perhaps the essence of Eleanor's strength was seeping through the wood and into her skin. "Now we shall never know if she would have explored the lands where you have never been or if she would have had a marriage far happier than mine has ever been."

"I will speak with Gideon." John's voice was harsh and ragged, and he stared at her as if he had never seen her before. "I will take a position at the general store as he has asked me to do. We could have another child."

John took a step closer and offered his hand, palm up, but Caroline only looked at it. She thought about John being here day after day, of looking at him and remembering all the years before while he did his best to forget they ever happened, of trying to pretend they could begin anew, and she brushed his hand aside.

"You may go to India," she said. "You may go to China. You may go to Hell for all I care. This is *my* house, and you are but a lodger who may come and go as he pleases."

Today, she would bury her daughter. Tomorrow, she would wear her sky dress and reshape her life without the mold of a husband to conform to. Perhaps she would learn from Eleanor and study maps instead of recipes.

"The Rum Barrel" is based on a real grave in the Old Burying Ground in Beaufort, North Carolina. These photos, taken by the author in 2013, show the gravesite. Find out more by following the QR code link.

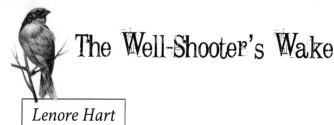

The Well-Shooter's Wake

Lenore Hart

Winters there were filled with death, frost like bitter icing on
wavy window glass, snow weighting frozen derricks like rent due
before payday. Every other week somebody's mother, kids clutching
her skirts, went slipping and sliding, following a pine box up
the cemetery's slope. Her sole talent knowing all the gestures,
the proper way to mourn, having practiced beneath the mountain's gray
shadow. Women widowed by thirty, without money to feed their own,
much less a bastard left-over like me.

The young men and old would take a dare, one last bloody chance,
and offer their bodies to the blasting fields, their pinched faces
to the stunning blows of a boxer's gloves. Nothing left to lose
but pocket-lint. No one could spare a dime. All the nuns at St. Bernard's
couldn't pray loud enough to impress heaven. And who fed
the children? Not Father Coughlin. Not John Rockefeller.
Any union man could describe what it's like to stuff newspaper
in the cracks of a shoebox company house, and still see snow
sift into the corners like cold sugar. To stare out at stacks and derricks
no longer belching smoke and ash and black oil. Quiet machines, empty
pipes, icy rail. No thunder, no work to be had on the mountain.

Drunk, my father once shouted, *I oughta strap nitro to myself
instead of the well, blow the whole fucking town to hell.* Instead
he slipped on a patch of ice near the whorehouse, headed home late
one night, after ten paid minutes in my mother's bed. Two days later
I followed his black parade up the mountain, a line of crows stitched
against icy white. Panting, ducking behind cracked headstones,
shadowing his dry-eyed wife, sullen kids. The pale resigned faces that
somehow never saw me. At school, his fat son and bucktoothed daughter
laughed at my clothes. They pretended not to see the family resemblance.

The mourners prayed, wiped their eyes, and went home
to eat cake. I stayed behind and watched two sweating men
cover my father with oil-black dirt.

Pandemonium

Celia Daniels

> *You can't keep a lady waiting forever,*
> *and there came an afternoon when she decided*
> *that she'd waited long enough.*
> —Orson Welles on Conchita Cintrón,
> *Memoirs of a Bullfighter*

1949, and Conchita dirties her pristine boots in the dust of a bullring in Jaén, Spain. She tastes

bile crawling up the back of her throat
salt from the sweat dripping off her nose
iron, a *rejoneadora* holding her horse's bit in her mouth

The crowd above her crows, rooster-red in the face. In the president's box, soldiers gather, each of them cradling an M43 La Coruña. Conchita presents them with her back, offering up an easy target.

Across the ring, her weary bull's horns gleam white.

Conchita reaches, smacks her horse, and sends him skittering out of the ring. She wiggles her toes in her shoes. Her *novillero* snaps something harsh in her ear; in response, she disarms him and sets his *muleta* against her hip. When he starts shouting, she uses it to knock him in the head. She hears

a child in the crowd weeping
the bull snorting and pawing as he circles
the clack of a dozen loaded Coruña breeches

Foam gathers in the crevices of the bull's snout. Conchita lets him size her up, his eyes obstinate obsidian.

She steps forward. She sets the *muleta* between them. She sees

hooves sinking deep as the bull tears the earth
the tip of her *estoque* gleaming
a mother in the crowd wringing her blistered hands

The bull charges. Conchita abandons her sword. The mother gasps; the child screams. The president's men aim their weapons, but the man doesn't say a word.

Conchita wields her *muleta*, draws the bull past her left side. As he goes, she drags a hand over the soft line of his shoulder. She feels

the dip of muscle
the quiver of bone
the gathering of dirt and sweat

and her fingers come away dirty.

Conchita Cintrón goes to the president's box when her bull is finally seizing and allows herself to be arrested. Female bullfighters are forbidden from fighting on foot, but when faced with the roaring crowd, Sr. Franco is forced to let the lady go.

That night, Conchita dips her *pan* in local olive oil. She savors

the chafe of her wrists
the rush of her blood
the crumbs of dirt still stuck between her toes.

Conchita Cintrón, 1948.

Way I Tell the Story

George Perreault

Use that feller's voice, high school catcher down Miami, say
Lefty, man was always half a bubble off, doesn't wait till he's
mowing 'em down the majors, talk about your own drummer—
was a time we're playing for the state title, up one in the ninth,
but needing the last out, bases full, three-two count, and Lefty

man, he steps off the mound, he's rubbing up that ball, just
staring into the sky like some old farmer praying for rain, like
there's nothing else in the world, ump telling me get out there,
let's wrap this thing, so I go ask him, hey, and he doesn't even
look down, says, you know, Billy, it's the longest time since

I been fishing, way those clouds coming in, blues they'll be
running hard tomorrow, so I say, Lefty, we gotta get this guy,
and he goes, no problem, slider down and away, but would you
maybe like to go fishing tomorrow, Billy, so I say yeah, you bet,
then go back, sit behind the plate, tell the ump my man's ready

and that ball comes cracking and hissing like lightning right
on the black, same pitch he rode to the Hall of Fame, and kids
all jumping up and down, going nuts, pounding each other and
hollering, except Lefty, dude's just shrugging it off, his eyes
weighing those clouds, he's already trolling blues in his mind.

Well, story like that, it's probably secondhand from a guy who
maybe knew a guy was sitting in the stands, but that don't matter,
not if you tell it with a shrug, lift your hands open . . . some stories,
hell, they just need to be true, all the best ones do, and anyway
there was this cat from the old Negro days, Cool Papa Bell. . . .

Lefty Gomez, 1936.

Bill Dickey, 1937.

James Thomas "Cool Papa" Bell, 1936.

Get the Story

Charissa Menefee

If we were reporters,
       we might be obsessed with the rocks.

How many were in Virginia's pockets?
Did she choose them carefully, one by one,
testing their smoothness, their weight,
or did she grab them by handfuls and cram
them, dirt sifting through her fingers, ripping
seams and bloodying her knuckles?

How close was she to the water when she
collected them? How many steps did she take,
pockets bulging, stones clattering against
each other, troubles incarnate, ragged points
poking her hips through the coat's lining and
the black twill skirt, scratching as she walked,
marking her with every stride.

If we were poets,
       we would wonder if she took off her shoes.

Virginia Woolf, c. 1927.

Blue and Green

Virginia Woolf

written in 1921

Green

The ported fingers of glass hang downwards [sic]. The light slides down the glass, and drops a pool of green. All day long the ten fingers of the luster drop green upon the marble. The feathers of parakeets—their harsh cries —sharp blades of palm trees—green, too; green needles glittering in the sun. But the hard glass drips on to the marble; the pools hover above the desert sand; the camels lurch through them; the pools settle on the marble; rushes edge them; weeds clog them; here and there a white blossom; the frog flops over; at night the stars are set there unbroken. Evening comes, and the shadow sweeps the green over the mantelpiece; the ruffled surface of ocean. No ships come; the aimless waves sway beneath the empty sky. It's night; the needles drip blots of blue. The green's out.

•

Blue

The snub-nosed monster rises to the surface and spouts through his blunt nostrils two columns of water, which, fiery-white in the center, spray off into a fringe of blue beads. Strokes of blue line the black tarpaulin of his hide. Slushing the water through mouth and nostrils he sings, heavy with water, and the blue closes over him dowsing the polished pebbles of his eyes. Thrown upon the beach he lies, blunt, obtuse, shedding dry blue scales. Their metallic blue stains the rusty iron on the beach. Blue are the ribs of the wrecked rowing boat. A wave rolls beneath the blue bells. But the cathedral's different, cold, incense laden, faint blue with the veils of madonnas.

Featured Writer

Kindra McDonald

Kindra McDonald is the author of the poetry collections *Fossils* and *In the Meat Years* (both in 2019) and the chapbooks *Elements and Briars* (2016) and *Concealed Weapons* (2015). She received her MFA from Queens University of Charlotte. She is an Adjunct Professor of Writing and teaches poetry at The Muse Writers Center in Norfolk, Virginia. She has been nominated for a Pushcart Prize and for *Bettering American Poetry*.

She was a resident at the Sundress Academy for the Arts in 2018, and in the fall of 2020, will be a Tupelo Press 30/30 featured poet. Her most recent work can be found at *SWWIM, Headline Poetry and Press,* and *300 Days of Sun.*

Much of her inspiration comes from nature and exploring trails, from her Dismal Swamp backyard to the Appalachians. She is slightly obsessed with Meriwether Lewis and the historical figures who forged into unknown territories. She spent 2019 hiking all of Virginia's state parks and is currently serving as a Resource Ranger in the Virginia Service and Conservation Corps. She never imagined she'd be handling snakes and tracking turtles, but it's all fueling her poetry, and she's working on her next collection inspired by her time in the woods.

Kindra is an unbalanced yogi, a baker still trying to master the macaron, a former amateur aerialist, a mixed-media dabbler who's thrown clay, blown glass, arranged flowers, and painted, but who always, always returns to poetry. She lives in the city of mermaids with her husband and cats. You can find her at kindramcdonald.com.

Last Ride of the Season—
Dismal Swamp Canal Trail

Autumn is the sound of tires spinning
over fallen leaves. The crunch
and rustle as they swirl through the gusty
rush of riding. November air speaks
into my ears until they ache.
Wind off Lake Drummond
drums my imagination, and I wonder how
old Bill managed to survive the expedition
here. Outliving the rest of his hunting
party, the lake now his namesake.

William Drummond,
c. 1617–1677.

His ghost in the fog follows
me this last night racing against sun-
down following the canal. Each crackle
of branches, each crush of rusted maples,
every stirring pushes me on. There is beauty
in this place despite its name.
Poets drawn to the mystery, the stark
cold of the air, the very spell of death.

Robert Frost, c.
1894, when he
walked into the
Great Dismal
Swamp.

That afternoon, no sun shone
through the thinning leaves, despair
led him to the romantic
sounding Dismal Swamp; Frost
somehow thought better
of his life as he leaned
over the bank, feet slipping in
the sand, his heart sprinting as he lost
balance. That split second he feared
the darkness closing over his head, the cold grip
on his lungs, he backed away and breathed
the moist air, leaves crushed beneath his feet.

Exiting the trail as the sun sets behind
the scolding gaze of the park ranger.
What does he do there in the dark?
If I stood in that very spot with Frost, my reflection
blinking up at me, the ghosts of the hunting
party urging me in, would I change my mind
or dive?

Grinder's Stand

You squint in the firelight sketching
out the new world
a canvas of chance.
You, greatest pathfinder,
quiet explorer by starlight.
You and your new brother, now
forever conjoined to your name;
a Siamese twin in history
with his few months' study of astronomy
and map making.

The quiet would build such pressure upon
the ear there was music in it.
Such open space all around, land and horizon,
just sky and the possibility of beyond. Winding
with the Snake and Salmon rivers you discover
what you were born to do.

After this, how could you sit
down to business, to govern? When always
there's the wider earth, the dark spaces to uncover.
And now so much noise, so much chatter,
and everything so small,
all paths already forged,
each wall closing in.
Coyotes in the shadows
howling from the corners.

Lewis, just you, alone pacing the wood
floors of this rented room.
Is it the land that's calling you?
Is it that great ocean and what's beyond it?
Or the scotch and the opium that dull your senses?
That moonless night how your hand shook
with the weight of the gun leaving you
cold in morning. You, now a memorial
lurking on an ancient trail
with every stone explored,
every patch of dirt memorized.

Captain
Meriwether
Lewis, 1807,
two years
before his
death at
Grinder's
Stand.

Maternal Bonds

I wash my daughter's feet with warm water
scented with eucalyptus and mint.
She has just woken from her nap
and I rub her arches and the insides
of her soles. Her grandmother kneels
on raw knees at the head of my daughter
and kisses her with a tenderness I do not feel.

As I break each of her toes one by one
tucking them under her foot
the tiny lily of gentility my mother
is there to clamp a hand over the mouth.
We work in silence, she and I, over our third
generation, gone limp with pain.

Think of the good marriage that will be arranged.
Her feet those of a tiny doll; those golden lotus feet will
be promises that carry her.

I wrap my little one's feet with cloth strips to
hold her toes in place, then with one swift moment,
like breaking the neck of a chicken, I break
her arches and pull her foot straight with her leg,
while Lao Lao holds her arms and hums an old
song to drown out the sounds.

She tells me this insured my own good life.
I continue winding the cloths around the feet
thinking of my own magnificent lies.

The bound feet of a
Chinese woman, c. 1890s.

Lack

Salt splits the sidewalks in cracks,
throws up chunks of concrete like loose
bricks, far more treacherous than the ice
it was meant to melt. In Northern towns
the roads wear the scars of salt.

Wars waged over this, empires gained
or lost, white grains found on altars
in pages of holy books, purity used
in exchange for slaves. The ones not worth
their salt were tossed.

Traded for silks, cumin, and people—
pork, beef, and fat, it preserves, cures and wounds.
Mourning tastes like salt, that ocean that never sates thirst.
Salt curing mummies aided the soul into the afterlife.
Pinched, thrown over the shoulder for luck,
or to ward off the Devil.

In the heart of February, far from home, I trace
ice patters like the corners of my grandmother's eyes,
her people, salt of the earth. Stepping slowly, I can't stop
thinking of Napoleon's troops marching in the cold retreat
from Moscow. How they died on snowdrifts, their wounds
unable to heal for lack of salt.

Napoleon's retreat from Russia, c. 1812.
Episode of the War of 1812 by Illarion Mikhailovich
Pryanishnikov (Илларио́н Миха́йлович Пря́нишников), 1874.

Lost Language

200 languages have become extinct in the last three generations, and an additional 199 have fewer than 10 speakers left. Some endangered languages, are being revived by young people and through poetry.
—United Nations Educational,
Scientific, and Cultural Organization

Shorter now than the lifespan of a mayfly
these words do not even mate.
Nothing left to paint a blue streak
as languages fade before alphabets can be written.
Their fragments fall to the ground as each native ages.
When all the speakers get together there is no one to
talk to. The word "we" has disappeared.

Walking past the graveyards, they collapse, their breath
held for miles. Oral tradition has lost a voice, a bitten
tongue as words turn to ash and dust in your mouth.
Rake charcoal from your chapped lips,
how they burn me with their heat. Lick
your mother tongue to find relief in your young ones,
poets sing this water, praise this balm.
It is there separating us, drink.

Yara ni 'Ua

Rebecca Pelky

I was built on the shore of this cove,
where you came and
I want to give you back the cargo of
puerto and portage, seco and bay.
the harbor, to scrawl
to say, go home. I want to claim
dragons really do hunt the bay.

To live, I forget the me
the ships, cocked like wanton fingers,
the coral reef, forget the fathers
first. I forget my selves,
and the genocide. You tried to say,
they were all already dead;
my body to sit on
my body to break

staked and claimed,
you gave things.
your names—
I want to tar
my own maps. I want
the spring as salted, and to say,

who was here before
breached
who found me
the survivor
the children in me,
You wanted
your shore, but also
the rough waves.

The Lakota Sioux

David S. Pointer

The Sioux

Now what in the world shall we dioux
With the bloody and murderous Sioux
Who some time ago
Took an arrow and bow
And raised such a hellabelioux?
                    —Eugene Field

What would our ears ever do
Without the fine and musical Sioux
        Who not so many songs ago
        Gave us Mister Buddy Red Bow
Who sang of the thunderbirds
And great buffalo herds, too?

Eugene Field, 1896.

Buddy Red Bow,
1948–1993.

Eugene Field wrote "Wynken, Blyken, and Nod" and was a famous children's poet. His poem was found in *A Special Collection: Illustrated Poems for Children*, Hubbard Press, Northbrook, Illinois, 1973. There's even a Eugene Field Elementary School in South Dakota.

David S. Pointer's maternal great-grandparents, Oscar Askew, most likely Choctaw, and Edna Wilson, the daughter of a plantation owner who had "lost everything" after the Civil War, shown here in their wedding photo, c. 1903. They were reported to be "hard-working farmers who didn't smoke or drink."

Coquille Ferry

Rebecca Pelky

Oregon Territory, January 28, 1854

Miners and citizens met yesterday
at this place, resolved

that the threat
of the Indians
of this place

called for action. Forty men
were raised to chastise the tribe.

We were perfectly successful.
Fifteen were killed.

We took all the women prisoner.
We took all the children prisoner.
We took all the old men prisoner
as far as was possible.

I think hostilities will be suspended
til your arrival, which I hope will be soon.

The Indians are in sight, hovering
around the ashes of their homes.

The Nasomah Massacre of 1854,
during which 40 white settlers attacked the sleeping village of the
Nasomah Indians at the mouth of
the Coquille River in Oregon, killing 15 men and 1 woman.

Brothertown

Rebecca Pelky

Mohegan, my ancestors sat on Cochegan Rock and smoked in four directions.
First they prayed east, where the sea brought the next age in sunrise and sails.
Then they prayed south, for warmth in harvest and friendship in Ojibwe lands.
Then they prayed west, for endings, and walked away from salted shores forever.
Then they prayed north, for the kind of cold that cleanses.

When they reached Lake Michigan, they must have seen the ocean—
if the ocean cast a shadow, surely it was here in this gray and green endless lake.
This is where they would become, dig their heels in the sand and say, here
we have taken our last stand. Brothertown,

my people sing of churches built in seven villages,
and when I am asked, who are the Brothertown Indians,
I answer that we are here, intermixed with the general mass of mankind.
I answer that I have heard the voices of the women who live under my skin.
I will answer only to them, the seventh direction, for my existence.

Samson Occom, c. 1770s, founder of
the original Brothertown Indian
settlement and first Native American to
have his writings published in English.

Brothertown
Indian Nation.

Letters, 1764 and 1771

Samson Occom

In 1743, a Congregational minister, orator, and educator in Connecticut by the name of Eleazar Wheelock took on Samson Occom as a student. Occom, a Mohegan who knew English, was a ready pupil, studying theology and learning to read and write in Hebrew. Occom was successful in bringing Mohegan students under Wheelock's wing, and Wheelock's success prompted him to found the Moor's Charity School to teach Native Americans. To raise funds, Wheelock sent Occom with empty pockets on a fundraising tour of England.

Letter to Eleazar Wheelock, September 8, 1764

I am Sorry you cou'd'nt get at Least Some Money for [us], it looks like Presumption for us to go on long Journey thro' Christians without Money, if it was altogether among Indian Heathen we might do well enough—But I have determined to go, tho' no white Missionary wou'd go in Such Circumstances—I leave my House and other Business to be done upon your Credit, and it will be Dear Business in the End,—if I hired one good Capenter and four other good Hands, any House woud have been forwarder than it is now, so the Best Judges tell me— [. . .] In a ward I leave my Poor Wife and Children at your feet. [A]nd if they hunger starve and die let them Die there[. . . .] This in utmost hast and with Sincere obedience, is from your Good for Nothing Indian Servant Samson Occom [all sic] [.]

Occom didn't keep money for himself and never got paid much, so his family often struggled and starved. Yet, when he returned from one of his long journeys of raising money and finding donors for the Moor's Charity School, he found that Wheelock had decided to "enlarge" the school. What this truly meant was: to take the fundraising money that Occom had raised for the education of young Native American boys and use it instead to found a new college for the sons of white English colonists. Despite opposition—from Occom, Native Americans, the British Board of Trustees, and all the donors who thought they were helping to educate young American Indians—Wheelock kept the donations, moved the school, designed classes for white college-aged boys in classics, philosophy, and literature, and became the college's president. That college was Dartmouth College. Wheelock's white son was in the first graduating class. In the first 200 years of Dartmouth's existence, there was a paltry total of 19 Native American graduates combined.

Letter to Eleazar Wheelock, July 24, 1771

[. . .] I am very Jealous that instead of Your Semenary Becoming alma
Mater, She will be too alba mater to Suckle the Tawnees, for She is already
a Dorn'd up too much like the Popish Virgin Mary[.] She'll be Naturally
asham'd to Suckle the Tawnees for She is already equal in Power Honor
and Authority to any College in Europe, I think your College has too much
wordly Grandure for the Poor Indians they'll never have much benefet of
it,—In So Saying I Speak the general Sentiment of Indians and English too
in these parts; a. so many of your Missionaries and School masters and Indian Scholars Leaving You and Your Service Confirms me in this opinion,
—b Your having So many white Scholars and So few or no Indian Scholars,
gives me great Discouragement—

I verily thought once that your Institution was Intended Purely for the poor
Indians[. W]ith this thought I Chearfully Ventur'd my Body & Soul, left my
Country my poor Young Family all my Friends and Relations, to Sail over
the Boisterous Seas to England, to help forward your School, Hoping, that
it may be a lasting Benefet to my poor Tawnee Brethren, with this View I
went to Volunteer—I was quite willing to become a Gazing stock, Yea Even
a Laughing Stock, in Strange Countries to Promote your Cause—we Loud-
ly Proclaimd before Multitudes of People from Place to Place, that there
was a most glorious Prospect of Spreading the gospel [. . .] to the furtherest
Savage Nations in the wilderness, thro' your Institution, we told them that
there were So many Missionaries & So many Schoolmasters already Sent
out, and a great Number woud Soon follow[. . . .]

But when we got Home behold all the glory had decay^d and now I am
afr'aid, we Shall be Deem'd as Liars and Deceivers in Europe, unless you
gather Indians quickly to your College, in great Numbers and not to have
So many Whites in the Charity,—I understand you have no Indians at Present except two or three Mollatoes— —this I think is quite Contrary to the
Minds of the Donors, we told them, that we were Beging for poor Miserable
Indians,—as for my part I went, purely for the poor Indians, and I Should
be as ready as ever to promote your School according to my poor Abilities
if I coud be Convinc'd by ocular Demonstration, that your pure Intention
is to help, the poor helpless Indians, but as long as you have no Indians, I
am full of Doubts,—

Your writing to Esqr Thornton to my Disadvantage and not one word in my
favour, gave me to think, that your Indian Scholars had reason to with
Draw from You, and Your Missionaries and Schol, Masters too, the opinion
of many white People about here is that You have been Scheeming alto-
gather, and that it was a [Pollicy] to Send me over to England, for (Say they)
now they don't Care anything about you, You have answerd their Ends,
now you may Sink or Swim it is all one to them, this makes me think of
what that great man of god Said to me, Mr Whitefield, just before I left

England in the hearing of Some gentlemen—ah, Says he, [. . .] You have been a fine Tool to get Money for them, but when you get home, they won't Regard you the'll [Set] you a Drift,—I am ready to believe it Now—

I am going to Say Some thing further, which is very Disagreeable Modisty woud forbid me, but I am Constraind So to write,—Many Gentlemen in England and in this Country too, Say, if you had not this Indian Bait, you woud not Collected a quarter of the Money you did, one gentleman in Particular in England Said to me, if he hadn't Seen my face he woudn't have given [yᵉ] happence but now I have £50 freely—This one Consideration gives me great Quietness, I think I went to England with Honest Heart, I think I have dont that which I think was my Duty to Do— [. . .] I wish I coud give you one visit, to have a ful talk but you got so far up, I Shall never be able [all sic] [. . . .]

The Founding of Dartmouth College, wood engraving by Samuel E. Brown, first published in 1841.

Eleazar Wheelock, c. 1769.

The Occom Circle documents at Dartmouth College Library.

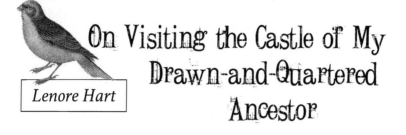

On Visiting the Castle of My Drawn-and-Quartered Ancestor

Lenore Hart

You don't approach it across broad green plain, or over drawbridge and moat, but down a narrow brick street lined with warehouses, a tall gray church, one crumbling Victorian brick façade, and a few modest houses with tiny, walled front gardens. Every front window frames a watchful cat. No doubt they also did in the 16th century, keeping the rats down, when my ancestor the mayor of Limerick still had a town, his head, and all his limbs. That was before death arrived with Cromwell: a prissy name for a Puritan Bible-beater who loved meting out cruel, bloody punishments.

On the next block I finally spot it, just ahead: the family fairytale made stone. But . . . so small! In my mind, Fanning's Castle always rose ancient but whole, sporting turrets, crenellations, huge arched windows; a senescent keep. In truth it's merely four jagged walls, a pile of gray blocks in a car park. Floor paved with weeds, dead grass, flakes of its own stony skin. At first that doesn't matter. For the 800-year-old walls are real, cold, gritty beneath my fingers. Pressing a palm to one square stone, I feel, or maybe imagine, a hum like an electric pulse. The crevices sprout green ferns and white flowers so tiny I've no choice but to believe they were planted by a fae gardener. The castle looks solid as a bulwark. It looks as if at any moment it will crumble to dust.

I take photos through the archers' slits. In 1651, these offered views of an English army bent on victory, spoils, and murder. All I see is two parked cars. Then, a ginger cat strolling past on some secret errand. Strange to think a man whose genes I carry also gazed out like this, once, and saw Death surging toward him: buzzcut Roundhead fanatics in leather armor and iron helmets, pikes and swords bristling, bringing Protestant jihad. In the end, Limerick fell. So Dominic Fanning kissed his wife goodbye, and surrendered. First hanged, he was then cut down. Each limb tied to a horse facing to the four winds. The animals whipped and shouted at until the mayor was torn, as we still say, limb from limb. His head, for good measure, mounted over St. John's Gate before a crowd: some crying, some jeering, some no doubt cheering.

I close my eyes to imagine that scene. Call up films, novels read,
even a past sojourn in a Shakespeare troupe. This merely evokes
movie violence, fake blood. Recorded, actorly screams. Feigned,
graceful deaths digitally enhanced for streaming. For truly, who
could live in a world such as that? Not us, not now. I traveled
to Ireland to feel closer to the past. But there's no way back,
despite genetics and shared names. Only a fleeting glimpse
of times vanished, castles fallen, a people long dead. Divided
by the astronomical distance of centuries, we act out our lives
upon the same stage. But the lines have been so often rewritten,
the scenery pulled down and repainted. The past refuses
to be known; it will never submit and be ours, in the end.
Only deign to hand us gaudy tourist brochures, instead of
the truth we'd so naïvely thought to conquer.

Fanning's Castle, 2017.

Oliver Cromwell, c. 1650s.

East Yorkshire Coastal Erosion (1965–Present)

Winston Plowes

I remember the 70s edge that wasn't.
A nose's bridge on the map's broken crease.
The cliffhanger slope where ammonites coiled,
sleeping in my infant's eye.
That slumped blockade between land and sea
where once I shuddered, ledged.

I remember the 80s
when it took ten steps back,
and caravans retreated
when buildings lost their footing.

I remember now that it was just an excuse
for the land to turn to sand.
That the sea can go back on its promise
to leave my memories be.

East Yorkshire coastline, near Mappleton, 2010.

Sunny Days— Protect and Survive

Winston Plowes

"Does the ice-cream van call here?"
your only link with the outside world

"Let us play hide and seek now"
It cannot be seen or felt

Mum watches the children from a window
we do not know what targets will be chosen

"Let us play at schools, in the barn"
the lives of your family may depend upon it

"First I will hear you sing"
the sirens will sound a steady note.

There are trees in the garden as well as flowers
falling where the wind blows

"Let us look for butterflies"
the most widespread dangers of all

"Look, little yellow chicks"
will be totally destroyed

Send the children to the fall-out room.
"Good-night," they say to their mother.

"We have had sun all the time"
the direct effects of the weapons

Peter looks up and sees Jane's head
Beyond that, there can be severe damage

"Dad has a new cricket bat"
If Britain is attacked by nuclear bombs

---

1) Ladybird book 8a, *Sunny Days* (The Ladybird Key Words Reading Scheme), W. Murray, 1964. 2) Home Office booklet, *Protect and Survive* (How to make your home and family as safe as possible under nuclear attack), The Central Office of Information, 1976 (Reprinted, 1980). One line from each of 1) and 2) per couplet. All original case and punctuation preserved.

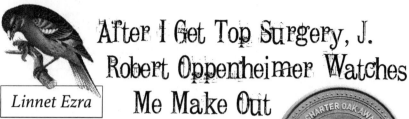

After I Get Top Surgery, J. Robert Oppenheimer Watches Me Make Out with My Partner

Linnet Ezra

he (my partner) tells me the drainage containers look like grenades

//

in 2010, during the Super Bowl Halftime Show™,
pop superstar and cultural appropriator extraordinaire
Katy Perry wears a contraption that shoots fireworks out of her
tits

//

i have to keep the drains in an extra week
i visit my partner and he wants me to be more naked
then corrects himself *no, be   comfortable*
i worry endlessly about the grossness of healing
correctly   the grenades bob between us   i
perch on my hip and hold my new chest (no tits) above
his   i think *this is the closest we have ever been*

//

the nurse unhooks the grenades from inside my
pockets, then   prepares to pull the drains out of
my rib-skin-area   i imagine snakes
          shedding or   a wet tentacle creeping around
                  the protagonist's hiding-place   an
alien-thing burrowed with sensitive bulbous fingers
the nurse   pulls the tube   is out before
                  i panic—

104

//

during preliminary tests for the atomic bomb, J. Robert
Oppenheimer thought the concept of a post-explosion
light-show a beautiful thing until   he realized
the opulence, too, would   kill

//

in a convergence of timelines, perhaps Oppenheimer would've
designed Katy Perry's boob-fire/works   picture a man
dazzled by a body wanting   to give it a brighter   memory
how to twitch the chest muscles or rather time the gadget
perfectly so that the explosion is   beautiful

//

after the drains are out, my mother asks me when
i'm medically allowed to have sex again   she means
when will it be safe to touch me   consensually she means
how will i stave off the   hungry   warmongers
or at what point will the radiation glow of my (new) body
dim enough not to horrify anyone deciding if they find me
      beautiful or   deadly—

//

my partner tells me i'm beautiful and Oppenheimer stops
      taking notes, watches   our hands float
toward each other like   membranes my throat
a bottle opener   my partner tells me he drowns in
      people, now i worry about   the drain-fluid leaking
out of my body its own   embarrassment   Oppenheimer
never forgave himself for being smart enough to create but
      not smart enough not to make   do you see
Oppenheimer sketches two machines moving against
      time   a bomb   exploding   my partner's mouth
a desert i wade through sometimes   i wonder who loved
Oppenheimer after   the war   who did he drag his bloody
hands home to who   wrung the towel out who
      mopped up   the flood

Let's Ask Leda about Consent

Rebecca Pelky

Would you, willingly, give yourself
to a bird? What's seductive
in webbed claws, a toothy beak
pushing past your teeth? Art only sees

white wings and that long arch of neck,
but the bruises haven't blued yet,
and paint can't breathe pain into my ribs,
and have you ever *seen* a swan penis?

At the clinic they forced me to see
shells nesting in the palms of my pelvis,
and I wish I'd begged the nurse for fists,
that I'd bled yolk. Instead, now,

each morning, I listen for Pollux to crow,
and I pluck Castor's elbows of down.
I taught Clytemnestra to wait,
that her face is a bird call.

I taught Helen to watch the gander,
the cob, how they fight.
I taught my daughters to hunt
and dress in turn their flocks of men.

Leda and the Swan, 16th-c. copy of the lost original by Michelangelo Buonarroti.

Jacob's Vision: We Stand at MoMA

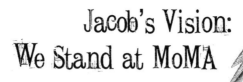

Lois Baer Barr

Your descendants will be like the dust of the earth,
and you will spread out to the west and to the east,
to the north and to the south.
—Genesis 28:14

And the migrants kept coming.
—Jacob Lawrence

Lawrence dreamed of Siqueiros, Orozco, and Rivera,
but he was twenty-three, and oil paint was dear.
The WPA paid him thirty bucks a week to paint
18 x 12-inch hardboard with milk tempera.

He saw the South, though he hadn't been there,
through a Harlem prism of Langston poems,
Savage sculpture, Schomburg books, Powell sermons.
Through his mother's stories; his father's absence.

Colors applied one by one. Black prison bars.
Smoky-gray Pittsburgh. Forest-green cloaks, umber
faces, ochre hats. Azure sky New York. Pink-
fisted labor agents. Ivory baby bonnets.

Marian Anderson's *Sweet land of liberty* rings
from a dark gallery. Lady Day's *blood on the leaves,*
blood at the root. My poem builds bit by bit.
He saw all sixty panels before he mixed his paint.

They journeyed for days. Many jailed 'til trains
left the station. We take a plane and a bus
to see Jacob's dream. Spy the museum's rooftop
from our hotel suite: no rocks for pillows here.

107

Blackbirds and cloudbirds all flying north.
Boll weevils and bloodied ropes stayed south.
Fatback south and hambone north. Newspapers,
letters said come, *And the migrants kept coming.*

Panel 35: They left the South in great numbers. They arrived in
the North in great numbers. Casein tempura on hardboard by
Jacob Lawrence, part of the Migration Series, 1940-41.
THE PHILLIPS COLLECTION, WASHINGTON, D.C.

Jacob Lawrence, 1941.

The Migration Series at
The Phillips Collection,
Washington, D.C.

Poem inspired by "One-Way Ticket: Jacob Lawrence's Migration Series and Other Visions of
the Great Movement North" exhibit at the Museum of Modern Art, April 3 to September 7,
2015, featuring work from MoMA and The Phillips Collection.

Featured Writer

Benjamin Goluboff

Benjamin Goluboff teaches English at Lake Forest College, and lives on the north side of Chicago. Over a long career he has produced scholarly work on American literature, as well as imaginative writing in four genres. On the scholarly side, Goluboff has written about Ken Kesey, Emily Dickinson, 19th-century travel writing, literature of the Vietnam War, and most recently, contemporary poets Michael Heller and D. A. Lockhart.

Goluboff's imaginative writing—poetry, fiction, essays, and drama—has appeared, among other places, in *Hayden's Ferry Review*, *Unbroken*, *The Museum of Americana*, *Jewish Currents*, *Tulane Review*, *Penn Review*, *The Cordite Poetry Review*, *War Literature and the Arts*, and *Misfit Magazine*. He is the author of *Ho Chi Minh: A Speculative Life in Verse*, and *Biking Englewood: An Essay on the White Gaze*, both from Urban Farmhouse Press.

In recent years, Goluboff has been working on speculative biographical poetry of the sort that is sampled here in *Footnote #4*. This is narrative verse that sometimes documents the facts of a biographical subject's life, sometimes departs from and embroiders upon those facts, inventing events and meetings that never happened outside the poet's imagination. In addition to patron of the arts John Quinn and photographer Walker Evans, poems on whom appear here, Goluboff's recent subjects include Air Force General Curtis LeMay, canonical songwriters Leiber and Stoller, and record producer John Hammond.

Goluboff enjoys writing collaboratively. His most recent article on Emily Dickinson, which involves the poet's botanical knowledge, was written with the biologist Glenn Adelson. Together with poet Mark Luebbers, he is at work on a suite of speculative biographical poems about Swiss photographer Robert Frank. Goluboff and his wife, the actor Cat Hermes, just saw their second 10-minute play produced.

During the Armory Show, John Quinn Suppresses a Toast

Quinn, who had lent the Exhibition
some 75 paintings from his collection,
helped arrange the rental of the 69th St. Armory,
and led a scandalized Teddy Roosevelt
from canvas to canvas down
the Exhibition's reeling corridors,
also bought all the champagne
for the Beefsteak Dinner, at Healy's, to which
The Association of American Painters and Sculptors
invited the gentlemen of the press.

The drink flowed freely (Quinn's favorite: Pol Roger)
and the toasts grew hilarious as the artists
matched wits with the journalists, until one wag
(we imagine him a minor disciple of Glackens
or Henri) proposed: "To the Academy!"
Jeers. Catcalls. Hissing. Laughter.
Never at a loss, Quinn leapt to his feet:
"No, no! Don't you remember Captain John Philip of the *Texas*?
When his guns sank a Spanish ship at Santiago,
he said, 'Don't cheer, boys, the poor devils are dying!'"

Armory Show, International Exhibition of Modern Art, the Cubist room, 1913.

John Quinn's Elegy

When, a week belated, news of Synge's death
reached Quinn in New York,
he paced the carpets of his bachelor rooms
in the grip of a fierce elegiac impulse.

All the old songs of loss
—"Thyrsis," "Adonais," "Lycidas"—
rang their chimes in Quinn's memory,
as a tension rose behind his eyes
like a cord twisted to knotting.

Sing of Synge, he sang, *tubercular and traduced*,
but he knew this was no good.

Incapable of elegy, the attorney
fell back on other powers.

In the days that followed
he caused the decedent's
Poems and Translations
to be privately printed
(correcting errors of punctuation
from the Yeats sisters'
Cuala Press version)
in a deluxe edition of fifty volumes:
forty-five on handmade paper
and five on vellum.

John Millington
Synge, 1905.

As he shipped these off to Dublin
for the playwright's friends and family,
the twisted cord behind Quinn's eyes relaxed,
almost as if he had, himself, sung.

John Quinn, c. 1913.

Walker Evans, Conservator of the Ephemeral, the Hypothetical, and the Mundane

In the Evans archive
at the Metropolitan Museum of Art
is a series of eighty-eight
prints and negatives
from the opening performance
at Madison Square Garden, 1942,
of "Circus Polka,"
the elephant ballet
Ringling Brothers
Barnum and Bailey
commissioned from
George Balanchine
and Igor Stravinsky.

Circus poster, Alabama,
photograph by Walker
Evans, 1935.

At Harvard
there are a half-dozen
photographs recovered
from Ben Shahn's
studio in 2000,
pictures Evans took
of preliminary sketches
for the suite of
reformist murals
Shahn planned
for the Rikers Island
prison complex,
before the project
was rejected in 1935
by New York City's
Municipal Art
Commission
on the grounds
of "psychological unfitness."

Portions of *The Meaning of Social Security* mural by Ben Shahn, c. 1939.

In the July 1955 issue of *Fortune* magazine a portfolio of Evans' photographs, "Beauties of the Common Tool," documents the "elegance, candor and purity" of, among others, the "T" Bevel, the Open-End Crescent Wrench, and the Baby Terrier Crate Opener.

General store interior, Moundville, Alabama, photograph by Walker Evans, 1936.

Walker Evans, 1937.

Bethlehem houses and steel mill, Pennsylvania,
photograph by Walker Evans, 1935.

Schoolhouse, Alabama,
photograph by Walker Evans, 1936.

Walker Evans Meets Ernest Hemingway, Havana, 1933

They met by accident at the *Floridita*
when the novelist heard someone
down the bar speaking American,
and for a week or so they drank together,
talking Art and Revolution.

Evans was in Havana
on commission for Carleton Beals,
shooting street scenes,
and making a file of atrocities.

(It was in Havana he learned
there was nothing that he could not look at,
not even what the *Machadistas*
left bloody on the ground,
so long as it was through a camera.)

Ernest Hemingway [ON LEFT] in Havana Harbor, 1934.

The novelist had come across from Key West
to breathe the atmosphere of danger in the *Floridita*,
to assume there a posture of resistance.

Evans was robbed his first night in town,
and the novelist lent him money
to stay and finish the job for Beals.
The novelist liked the kid,
thought he was a good listener.

In what can only be supposed
an act of deference,
submission even,
Evans never photographed the novelist.

But in two of his street scenes
he included Havana picture theaters
where *Adios a las Armas* was on the marquee.

Plaza del Vapor, Havana, Cuba, photograph by Walker Evans, 1933.

115

Walker Evans Photographs Signs

Two men load DAMAGED onto a flatbed truck,
midtown Manhattan, morning light.

On a hoarding in Charleston,
by a picture of Carole Lombard:
LOVE BEFORE BREAKFAST.

Chicago, State Street,
the sidewalks rain-slick
like Caillebotte's Paris:
WHAT! NO GARTERS?

LUCKY STRIKE: IT'S TOASTED
say the lights of Times Square.

In an interview late in life, Evans
would acknowledge that his technique
derived from Flaubert,
citing "the nonappearance of the author,
the non-subjectivity."

New Orleans street corner, Louisiana, photograph by Walker Evans, 1936.

New Orleans downtown street, Louisiana,
photograph by Walker Evans, 1935.

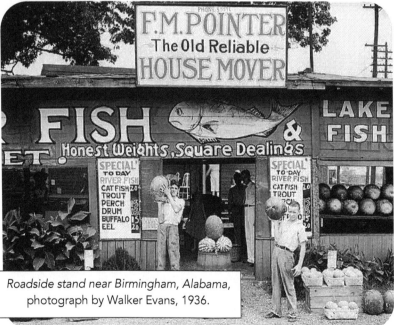

Roadside stand near Birmingham, Alabama,
photograph by Walker Evans, 1936.

John Quinn (1870-1924), collector of modern art and patron of modern artists, was one of the organizers of the 1913 Armory Show. Read more about him in *The Man from New York: John Quinn*, by B. L. Reid. One of the greatest photographers of the 20th century, Walker Evans (1903-1975), is the subject of a masterful biography by James R. Mellow.

117

DaguerreoTyped

Writers respond to our DaguerreoTyped historical ekphrastic photo prompt. The three following pieces address the image above.

One of These Days

Colin Patrick Ennen

When she was eight years old, Penelope Cartwright sent a letter to her father, then fighting on a battlefield in Virginia to preserve the Union, in which she asked him why it was—not how—he had survived so long. She was the only girl she knew, Penny explained, whose entire set of parents still lived. "I'd like to join their little club, Papa," she wrote with exquisite penmanship.

Twenty years later, her mind worked in much the same way. Which was why she had proposed a merry photo with her baby after the boring normal one had been taken. "Just something silly," she'd giggled. Oh, she'd expected the gasps and objections, of course. Rolled her eyes when they came: from the photographer, her aged mother, the nanny. Let-them-have-their-say had been her policy for ages. She'd get her way in the end, however. She always did.

And gosh darn it if she hadn't even mentioned specifics yet.

"Think of what he'll say when he's grown," her mother pleaded. "And your husband not a month dead." She clicked her tongue three times.

Penny cackled. Attuned to his lifegiver, the baby joined her in mirth. The nanny choked back a sob. So emotional, Penny thought.

"Oh, mother," she scoffed. "Mother, mother, mother. He is *my* child, after all." She shook her head, rising from the settee, handing little William to Miss Lavery. Still laughing, she made her way from the parlor and ascended to the nursery.

You see, the girl had been born a prankster. Inappropriate jokes were her milieu before she could even lace up her boots without sticking out her tongue. For instance, her father had not been the least bit surprised when he read her wartime letter. After all, the girl *had* sewn into his uniform jacket the wrong address for if he were killed and needed to be shipped home: that of a butcher in New York.

Oh, but Penelope was beyond adorable as a lass. Eyes bright blue beaming above plump cheeks and an upturned nose, curly brown hair bouncing as she hopped. The girl never walked or ran if she could hop.

"Nobody can trip me if I'm hopping," she reasoned.

"Why would anyone want to trip you, darling?" her mother had asked.

Penny had begun this early, before her fifth birthday. "To see my head smash open, obviously," the little cherub had replied.

She employed such conveyance once across town to her grandmother's house. In a tizzy, she turned heads along the way with her bouncing and wailing. Young Penelope burst through the ornate front doors of the palatial home, startled the ancient butler three-quarters of the way toward his death, and screamed that her mother—the grandmother's daughter—had fallen down the stairs at home and wasn't breathing. In seconds, the carriage was horsed, the doctor called for, the old lady and the young girl trundled off to the tragic scene. Imagine everyone's surprise, then, when the rescue party arrived to find the woman singing to her newborn in the garden, Penny howling in the background.

Merely the most public of her canards.

In the nursery upstairs, in the house that now belonged to her, she chuckled at the memory; she relished the thought of sharing such jests with William as he grew. Penny was rummaging through his trunk in search of a prop for their photo, humming to herself, feeling quite cheerful despite the mood downstairs. She had just had it yesterday. . . . Ah, there it was. So small. So familiar. So lifeless.

Outside, a hound barked, taking her back again:

Just before her father had returned from the war, as she sat bored indoors on a rainy Saturday afternoon, looking for mischief, Penelope managed to trap the family dog—a little black-and-white mutt—between two pieces of furniture in the parlor. As the mongrel yelped and flailed, and before the nanny or her mother could intervene, she yanked with all her might on the poor beast's tail. Though her goal had been complete detachment, what she managed was mere dislocation. The animal never wagged properly again.

Trouble never found the girl, however, even after that. Whether it were her angelic appearance, her softly spoken denials, or her pleas of ignorance, Penny always seemed to weasel her way out of discipline for any misdeed. To be sure, she more than once convinced her mother that some offense had in fact been undertaken by her younger sister, never mind the child could barely walk, or that the transgression had been simply a terrible mistake. Often, they were brushed off altogether.

One example, which ought to have gotten her flogged at least, was the occasion, not long after her father returned from the war, when he suggested they stroll—he stroll, she hop—down to the river for a fishing expedition. A getting-to-know-each-other-again adventure. He may also have harbored ideas of straightening her out.

Well, the colonel kissed that plan goodbye when, after asking young Penny to hand him a new worm, she instead brought forth a small pink finger. One of her sister's tiniest, as it happened.

Yes, only one of them found that little stunt amusing. Before running to check on his other daughter, Pa merely said what he always did: "One of these days. . . ."

It was never mentioned again.

Back in the present, Penny covered her quarry in a white lace shawl, cradling it under her arm as she rejoined the crowd in the parlor. Old Mrs. Cartwright, plump and grumpy, held hushed conference with Miss Lavery, the babe in the latter's arms looking as bored as the ladies were worried. Mr. Ashburn, tinkering silently with his camera, tried too hard not to eavesdrop.

Like them, Penny was in black. *Unlike* them, she wished she weren't. How long did she have to mourn her husband, anyway? It had been a month, after all. Twice as long as she'd been forced to "grieve" years before when her toddler brother had passed. Of course, she'd been there for that. She'd watched the boy die, actually—something she'd felt had given her a head start on the mourning period. But no.

She wondered, did Mr. Ashburn know that his father had, as sexton eighteen years before, accused that young, headstrong girl of defiling that very boy's grave? Did he know the significance of what she carried?

If Penelope had one weakness, it was an inability to mask her emotions. As such, when she entered the parlor, shawl bundled carefully in the crook of her arm, she struggled to conceal her giddiness at the prospect of imminent tomfoolery. She also hoped her mother might guess.

"Wipe that smile off your face, Penelope," Mrs. Cartwright barked. "I swear, young lady, one of these days you're—"

As if unveiling a sculpture, Penny removed the shawl from the skull with flourish, holding the relic toward Mrs. Cartwright, not even bothering to disguise her glee. Small, pale, cold-looking, the tiny cranium almost shined in the gaslight. The old woman started backward into a screen, knocking it to the ground. Miss Lavery nearly let fall little William. Mr. Ashburn hugged his camera to keep it safe.

"Thomas?" The old woman went white.

That was fast, Penny thought.

The old woman gasped and covered her mouth. Breath coming in gulps, Mrs. Cartwright shuffled two steps toward the skull in her daughter's hand. Thinking better of it, she retreated, first to the side of Miss Lavery, who also huffed for air, then to the parlor doorway, then to the hall, where her footsteps scuffled away to the front door. After a slam, attention turned to the child.

The baby had started to laugh before his mother this time, loud, squealing laughter, accompanied by flapping arms and flying spittle. Now it was Penny's turn to join in, offering a healthy guffaw and a wink to her progeny. As the room recovered from the revelation, however, and quieted, the child continued roaring, more high-pitched sounds escaping as his face reddened. The nanny held the baby away from her trembling body.

"He's scaring me," she whimpered.

Penny put down the skull and took the babe.

"Was that funny?" she asked him.

The child finally settled as she showered him with kisses. Shifting William to her knee, balancing him, she carefully removed the lower jaw from the skull, which she'd long ago wired on so it could move yet stay attached. This, of course, had provided for the only conversations she'd ever had with her brother. Conversations. Scoldings. A semantic quibble.

Penny then removed the bone panel she had cut away the previous day, leaving a gaping hole in the bottom of the skull. Not having measured, however, when she placed the bone structure upon William's soft head, it did not quite fit.

"Damn!" Penny bit her lip. She made several ponderous expressions in succession, then exploded with a smile. "Find me string, Miss Lavery."

The nanny choked on her breath. When she coughed next, little William giggled again. Miss Lavery ran from the parlor.

"Just bring me string!" cried her employer. "Mr. Ashburn, please set up your camera. I will sit here, holding the child like this." Penny posed in the chaise with little William looking over her left shoulder at the photographer.

Moments later the nanny returned, shaking and sniffling, whimpering like—well, like the puppy from Penny's childhood. Nevertheless, Miss Lavery carried a roll of string and a pair of scissors. Handing them to Penelope, she retreated behind Mr. Ashburn to weep. As if that would help.

Penny hummed again as she measured string by eye, cut, tied it to the skull in two places. "Oh, this *will* be fun," she whispered to William, silent and lolling on her knee.

Behind her Mr. Ashburn prepared his equipment, swatting away the nanny's shaking hands in spite of his obvious crush. Lifting the infant into place, Penelope wedged the skull on top of his little head, holding the two pieces of string in her hands to keep it steady.

"Do it now," she instructed. "He's stopped fidgeting."

The poof of the powder. The plate sliding out.

"Come get him, Miss Lavery. I think he's gone to sleep."

Silence.

"Come get him, Miss Lavery," Penelope growled, holding the baby out away from her body. The skull clattered to the floor.

A scream from behind, the camera crashing to the ground. Two pairs of footsteps running from the room. Deeper silence. The deepest, with only her heartbeat in her ears to intrude.

"Now what could—" Penelope looked at her still son and promptly dropped him.

The Hollow's Head Man

Ken Gosse

As an infant he nursed at the breast
of a harpy whose fierce, feathered chest
seethed venom most toxic.
It's not paradoxic
her face ensconced Xanthippe's crest.

While dressed in a raiment quite mild,
by which all the monks were beguiled,
this camouflaged habit
helped her snatch the abbot
encharged with the care of the child.

By malevolent rights of her coven,
he was cooked in an ancient Dutch oven.
Chicken soup for dead souls,
it burned hotter than coals.
Incantations of "Nothin' says lovin'."

He was bathed in this warm, bloody soup,
and his first sip of milk had a scoop.
This miasma of verma
expunged epiderma—
his vertex would never recoup.

As a young lad he envied good Yorick,
his younger friend, also folkloric,
who kept skin and head
'til long past he was dead
as we've learned from hist'ries categoric.

Then one day he went up a high hill
with young Eve (though the song calls her Jill),
but when they laid down
(hers long lost), lost his crown—
'midst the blueberries, he found his thrill.

Since then, he has worn a dark cloak,
and his hood covers pate of hard oak.
Eerie grin carved by hand,
as he travels the land,
he can scythe-up your soul with one stroke.

The Grim Reaper, who can't get ahead,
wants a skull, though his body is dead.
In Sleepy, Ohio,
he rode a caballo
but got jack-o'-lanterns instead.

He was there 'fore the first war'd begun;
he ran both the Big Wars, II and I.
From Genghis' sorrow
'til long past tomorrow,
no man is exempt 'neath the sun.

When all's said and done, none surmounts
the Dark Artisan, yet he discounts
all his skills with his tools
for he tells all us fools,
"It's the Scythe of the Reaper that counts."

Athanasia

Marion Lake

I trace the dull filigree of your hair with a fingertip, lonely,
tinted saffron from the iodine, a tattoo of death.
There is an iron smell of winter, of burnt coal fires, and the violent

hush of dusty curtains parting in the draft. They whisper vicious
dealings, like the chiming of those church bells
every quarter hour, marking time.
I hide the locket under my tongue and taste the comforting, cold
deadweight of it.

There is the nightly squeaking of wheels on the parquet floor
And tea and bitter toast, forgotten tableside—
the deadbolt thundering shut.
And through this heavy twilight, the mocking scent of velvet roses,
the lovely thought of your cherub handprint still impressed upon my breast.

You are loved, deathless, a victory.

Author Biographies

ARTHUR ALLEN is a British-Canadian poet currently reading for a PhD at the University of Edinburgh. His debut verse-novel, *The Nurseryman* (Kernpunkt Press, 2019), won the 2020 Eyelands Book Awards Poetry Prize. His poetry has previously appeared in several international publications including: *Ambit, Amsterdam Quarterly, The Bombay Review,* and *Tahoma Literary Review.*

LOIS BAER BARR is a literacy tutor in Chicago and an emerita professor at Lake Forest College. Her chapbooks of poetry and flash fiction are *Biopoesis* and *Lope de Vega's Daughter.* Twice nominated for the Pushcart Prize, she was a finalist for the Rita Dove Poetry Prize in 2019.

L. SHAPLEY BASSEN is a native New Yorker who reads for Craft Literary. She has won prizes and published stories, novels, poetry, plays, and book reviews. Her book of collected poetry, *What Suits a Nudist,* was published by Clare Songbirds Publishing House in 2019. Find her online at lsbassen.com.

DEMISTY D. BELLINGER lives and teaches in Massachusetts. Her chapbook, *Rubbing Elbows,* is available at Finishing Line Press. You can learn more about DeMisty at her website: demistybellinger.com.

BILL BERLINO grew up in Troy, New York, and graduated from Middlebury College in Vermont, where he developed a passion for nature and poetry. He has been teaching literature and drama and coaching for the past two decades, just north of Boston. He learns more from students and players than they do from him.

J. BOWERS is an Assistant Professor of English at Maryville University in St. Louis, Missouri. Her historical fiction has appeared in *StoryQuarterly, Redivider, The Portland Review, Big Muddy,* and other national journals.

ROBERT BUSBY lives, writes, runs, and teaches in Memphis, Tennessee, with his wife and their two boys. His fiction has appeared in *Arkansas Review, Cold Mountain Review, Flash! Writing the Very Short Story* (W. W. Norton), *Mississippi Noir* (Akashic), *Pank, Sou'wester,* and *Surreal South '11* (Press 53).

CELIA DANIELS is a ghostwriter with an MA in English Literature from the University of Toledo. Her included piece was originally crafted after she'd graduated from Indiana University Bloomington in 2017.

COLIN PATRICK ENNEN writes from Albuquerque, New Mexico, and works at a doggie daycare. His stories have appeared in two volumes from B-Cubed Press (*More Alternative Truths* and *Alternative Theologies*), on the website *Writers Resist,* and in the 2018 *Sage Anthology* from SouthWest Writers. He's on Twitter at @cpennen.

LINNET EZRA (they/them) is an Aries from the Jersey Shore whose recent accolades include winning *Sundog Lit*'s inaugural collaboration contest, hosting the 2017 Texas Grand Slam final stage, and acceptance into the 2017 *Bettering American Poetry* anthology. Their chapbook, *Bloodmuck,* was published by *The Atlas Review* (2018).

MIKE FOX's stories have appeared in journals in Britain, Ireland, America, Australia, and Singapore. His stories "Breath" (*Fictive Dream*) and "Blurred Edges" (*Lunate Fiction*) gained Pushcart Prize nominations. His story "The Homing Instinct" (*Confingo*) was included in *Best British Short Stories*. Find him at polyscribe.co.uk and on Twitter at @polyscribe2.

BENJAMIN GOLUBOFF teaches at Lake Forest College. In addition to scholarly publications on American literature, he has placed imaginative writing in many small-press journals. He is the author of *Ho Chi Minh: A Speculative Life in Verse*, and *Biking Englewood: An Essay on the White Gaze*, both from Urban Farmhouse Press.

KEN GOSSE prefers writing traditional rhyming verse. He was first published in *First Literary Review–East* in 2016, and since then by *The Offbeat, Pure Slush, Home Planet News Online*, and others. Raised in the Chicago suburbs, now retired, he and his wife have lived in Mesa, Arizona, for over twenty years.

VERNITA HALL is the author of *Where William Walked: Poems about Philadelphia and Its People of Color*, winner, Grand Prize for Poetry (Willow Books) and the Robert Creeley Prize (Marsh Hawk Press). With an MFA in Creative Writing from Rosemont College, she serves on the poetry board of *Philadelphia Stories*.

LENORE HART is the author of eight novels and numerous short stories, poems, and essays. She's received awards, grants, and fellowships from the NEA, the Oberpfalzer Kunstlerhaus in Germany, the VCCA, and several state arts councils and universities. She's on the faculty of the MFA program at Wilkes University, and at the Ossabaw Island Writers Retreat.

MARION LAKE is a writer from Colorado. Her short stories and poetry have been published in *The Copper Nickel, Crannóg, Pour Vida*, and *Weaving the Terrain*, an anthology of 100-word poems about the southwest. Marion teaches English at the secondary level and spends her free time skiing, playing with her kids, and daydreaming.

KINDRA MCDONALD is the author of the poetry collections *Fossils* and *In the Meat Years* and the chapbooks *Elements and Briars* and *Concealed Weapons*. She received her MFA from Queens University of Charlotte. She is an Adjunct Professor of Writing and teaches poetry at The Muse Writers Center in Norfolk, Virginia.

CHARISSA MENEFEE is a multi-genre writer and theater artist. Her poetry is published in literary journals, anthologies, and her collections with Finishing Line Press: *When I Stopped Counting* and *It Rains in My Sun Room*. She is also the founder and artistic director of The EcoTheatre Lab. Find her at charissamenefee.com.

REBECCA PELKY has a PhD from the University of Missouri, where she studied poetry and Native American literature. She is an enrolled member of the Brothertown Indian Nation of Wisconsin. Her first collection of poetry, *Horizon of the Dog Woman* (Saint Julian Press), was released in early 2020.

GEORGE PERREAULT has worked as a visiting writer throughout the American West, and his work has appeared in journals and anthologies in the U.S. and internationally. Perreault's latest book, *Bodark County*, is a collection of poems in the voices of characters living on the Llano Estacado in rural Texas.

WINSTON PLOWES lives aboard his floating home in Calderdale with his lucky black cat, Fatty. He teaches creative writing and was Poet in Residence for The Hebden Bridge Arts Festival 2012-14. His collection of surrealist poetry, *Telephones, Love Hearts & Jellyfish*, was published in 2016 by Electric Press.

DAVID S. POINTER is the author of *Beyond Shark Tag Bay*. David Currently resides in Murfreesboro, Tennessee, and will be attempting to relocate to Missouri or Kansas in the near future.

ANGELA RAPER is a writer from North Carolina who specializes in Southern contemporary and historical fiction and creative nonfiction. She earned her MFA in Creative Writing from Converse College, and she teaches at East Carolina University. When she isn't writing, she enjoys reading, knitting, and spoiling her pets.

ROGER SIPPL survived Hodgkin's Lymphoma as a teenager. After graduating from Berkeley, he IPO'd three software companies, also an adventure. Sippl studied creative writing at University of California–Irvine, Berkeley, and Stanford Continuing Studies. He's been published in dozens of journals, including *The Ocean State Review* and *The Bacopa Literary Review*. Find him at rogersippl.com.

ROBERT WALTON is a retired middle school teacher and a rock climber with ascents in Yosemite and Pinnacles National Park. His published writings include works of science fiction, fantasy, and poetry. Walton's historical novel, *Dawn Drums*, won New Mexico's 2014 Tony Hillerman Prize for best fiction. Find him at chaosgatebook.wordpress.com.

DAVID WHORLEY has published widely on matters related to public policy, international affairs, and diplomatic history. He lives in Ottawa, Ontario, Canada.

The 2018 Charter Oak Award

Alternating Current is dedicated to nurturing and promoting the independent press and its authors. We proudly honor our authors with annual writing awards, including the Charter Oak Award for Best Historical.

Legend has it that this unusually large white oak tree on what early colonists named Wyllys Hyll in Hartford, Connecticut, was where the Royal Charter of 1662 was shoved into a hidden hollow to thwart its confiscation by the English governor-general who wished to revoke the piece of legislation that granted autonomy to the colonists. This tree, named the Charter Oak, has since become a symbol of the power of documents and recorded history, the freedom they give us, showcasing the lengths one would go to protect, to defend, and to stand by words that could forever change the course of people's lives. While the Charter Oak is a strong, undeniable piece of American history, its symbol is universal. Words empower us all, the whole world over, and we'll die to protect our collective right to them. Alternating Current wants to preserve and reward those words that empower us, so that they, too, may go down in history.

The Charter Oak Award for Best Historical is awarded annually to a single piece of work that is historical in nature. The winning piece receives print publication in *Footnote;* online listings on our website; complimentary copies of the *Footnote* print journal with the winning piece indicated with our medallion imprint; a certificate; a cash honorarium; and our virtual medallion with permission for use on the author's websites and/or any published books or online outlets. A second and a third place and nine finalists receive print publication in *Footnote;* publication on our online journal, *The Coil;* and other prizes. Full details can be found at our website.

The finalists are selected by December each year and announced the following year, with the annual release of the corresponding issue of *Footnote.* The 2018 judging process consisted of submissions being sent incognito to the history editors, where the finalists and top pieces were determined.

Acknowledgments

Special acknowledgment to Devin Byrnes and SuA Kang at Hardly Square, for their creativity in designing our Charter Oak Award medallion imprint. Hardly Square is a strategy, branding, and design-based boutique located in Baltimore, Maryland, that specializes in graphic design, web design, and eLearning courses. Their invaluable design expertise has made our annual awards come to life. Find out more about them at hardlysquare.com.

Alternating Current Press wishes to acknowledge the following publications where pieces from issue No. 4 first appeared:

"My Man Richard" was previously published in the 2014 Moonstone *Anthology of Featured Readers* and in *Where William Walked: Poems about Philadelphia and Its People of Color.*

"Nights Spent Flying" was previously published on *The Coil.*

"June 19, 1865" was previously published in *VerseWrights.*

"July Haiku" was previously published in *Right Hand Pointing #48* and in *What Suits a Nudist.*

"The Well-Shooter's Wake" was previously published in a shorter version in *subTerrain.*

"Grinder's Stand" and "Lost Language" were previously published in *Fossils.*

"Lack" was previously published in *In the Meat Years.*

"After I Get Top Surgery, J. Robert Oppenheimer Watches Me Make Out with My Partner" was previously published on *The Coil.*

"Jacob's Vision: We Stand at MoMA" was previously published in *Valley Voices #19.2.*

"One of These Days" was previously published on *The Coil.*

"Athanasia" was previously published on *The Coil.*

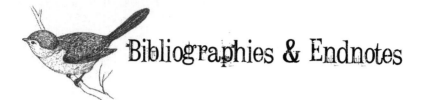

Bibliographies & Endnotes

"My Man Richard" drew references from the following sources: 1.) Richard Allen, *The Life, Experience, and Gospel Labours* [sic] *of the Rt. Rev. Richard Allen: To Which Is Annexed the Rise and Progress of the African Methodist Episcopal Church in the United States of America: Containing a Narrative of the Yellow Fever in the Year of Our Lord 1793: With an Address to the People of Colour* [sic] *in the United States* (Martin & Boden Printers, Philadelphia, 1833). 2.) Gary B. Nash, "New Light on Richard Allen: The Early Years of Freedom," *The William and Mary Quarterly*, Third Series, Vol. 46, No. 2 (April 1989), p. 332-340.

"The Wreck of the *Annabelle Lee*" author's note: Good history reveals unanswered questions—some of which may never be answered satisfactorily. That's where fiction steps in. I've written nine stories about Joaquín Murrieta's adventures subsequent to his disappearance from the public stage. My sources include Frank F. Latta's excellent book, *Joaquín Murrieta and his Horse Gangs*, Ireneo Paz's *Life and Adventures of the Celebrated Bandit Joaquín Murrieta: His Exploits in the State of California*, and Walter Noble Burns' dashing *The Robin Hood of El Dorado: The Saga of Joaquín Murrieta, Famous Outlaw of California's Age of Gold*.

"During the Armory Show, John Quinn Suppresses a Toast" contains a quotation in the last lines that is referenced from B. L. Reid, *The Man from New York: John Quinn and His Friends* (Oxford University Press, New York, 1968), p. 152.

"The Hollow's Head Man" author notes: The concept, including the title and the imaginary town of Sleepy, Ohio, was inspired by Washington Irving's 1820 short story, "The Legend of Sleepy Hollow." The phrase "Chicken soup for dead souls" is based on the title of the book series, *Chicken Soup for the Soul*, started in 1993, by Jack Canfield and Mark Victor Hansen. The phrase "Nothin' says lovin'" comes from the motto for Pillsbury biscuits from their television ads that began airing in 1965. The phrase "hist'ries categoric" is borrowed from "The Major General's Song" from Gilbert and Sullivan's 1879 operetta, *Pirates of Penzance*. The line "'midst the blueberries, he found his thrill" is based on the lyrics to the 1940 song "Blueberry Hill," featuring music by Vincent Rose and lyrics by Larry Stock and Al Lewis.

Colophon & Permissions

The edition you are holding is the First Print Edition pressing of this publication.

Our *Footnote* logo is set in an Alternating Current-created font. The subfont on the cover is set in Old Newspaper Types, created by Manfred Klein. The back cover Alternating Current Press font is set in Portmanteau, created by JLH Fonts. The number "4" of the title pages is set in Hightower Text, created by Tobias Frere-Jones, loosely based on the printing of Nicolas Jenson in Venice in the 1470s. The interior title font is set in Conrad Veidt, created by Bumbayo Font Fabrik. All image caption and editor-note text is set in Avenir Book, created by Adrian Frutiger. Place markers for the Charter Oak Award are set in Alcubierre, created by Matt Ellis. All other fonts are set in Athelas, created by Veronika Burian and Jose Scaglione, inspired by British fine book printing.

Cover artwork designed by Leah Angstman using images from the 1889 issue of the annual French magazine, *Figaro Illustré*. The Alternating Current lightbulb logo was created by Leah Angstman, ©2006, 2020 Alternating Current. The Charter Oak Award medallion was created by SuA Kang and Devin Byrnes of Hardly Square, for Alternating Current's sole use. Hardly Square logo ©2020 Hardly Square, hardlysquare.com. The Charter Oak silhouette courtesy Clker.

Stokely Sturgis' Bible image courtesy Smithsonian Institution National Museum of American History and Caroline L. and Nelson C. Simonson, under CC0 license. Enslaved women image courtesy *Harper's New Monthly Magazine*, Vol. 14 (1857), p. 438. Gore shooting Demby image courtesy *Life and Times of Frederick Douglass: His Early Life as a Slave, His Escape from Bondage, and His Complete History to the Present Time* (Park Publishing Co., Hartford, 1881), digitized courtesy *Documenting the American South*. Hoof of fire horse #12 photographed by Richard W. Strauss, courtesy Smithsonian Institution National Museum of American History and the District of Columbia Fire Department, 1902; used with permission under CC0 license. Catalog card image courtesy Smithsonian Institution National Museum of American History, under CC0 license. Engine Co. 9 photo courtesy Los Angeles Fire Department Historical Archive. Mack the Noble Fire Horse photo courtesy Library of Congress. David Livingstone book illustrations courtesy Princeton Rare Books Division. The Rum Keg Girl grave photographed by Angela Raper; used with permission. Conchita Cintrón photographed by Mariano Carmelo Rodríguez Núñez, under CC Attribution-Share Alike 3.0 Unported license: creativecommons.org/licenses/by-sa/3.0/deed.en; photo corners were rounded. Bill Dickey photo courtesy Harris &

alternatingcurrentarts.com

Made in the USA
Middletown, DE
04 December 2021

53424720R00085